C000161654

THE POWER OF MINDFULNESS AND SELF-HEALING

40 Ways to Remove Stress and Reclaim
Your Inner Peace and Happiness

Tamsin Cooper
Master Hypnotherapist

www.tamsincooper.co.uk

tamsin@tamsincooper.co.uk

The Power of Mindfulness and Self-Healing

40 Ways to Remove Stress and Reclaim your Inner Peace and Happiness

Tamsin Cooper
Master Hypnotherapist

Copyright ©2020 TamsinCooper

Cover Design by germancreative

Edited by Aysha Khan

Little Owl Cards 2 can be bought from www.littleowlonline.co.uk

The information in this book is not to be used as a substitute for medical assistance and the author cannot accept any responsibility for any health issues that may arise from following her advice.

First Printing February 2021

ISBN 978-1-8383884-0-9

Website www.tamsincooper.co.uk

Tamsin Cooper is available worldwide to help you to overcome anxiety or stress related issues. Email in the first instance tamsin@tamsincooper.co.uk

Why Read This Book

Whether you have recently been suffering from anxiety or stress or you have been suffering for many years this self-help book can help you.

If you read this book you will move from a place of stress or anxiety to a place of calmness and peace.

Almost every leading book on stress and anxiety explains the value of mindfulness but only a few of them focus on the detailed techniques that can be used to practice mindfulness.

This book contains easy-to-learn mindfulness techniques using exercises, meditations, tasks, and affirmations that can transform your life instantly and minimise your unresourceful thoughts and feelings in 40 ways.

I am hopeful that as you continue to read this book, you will move from a place of stress or anxiety to that place of calm and peace.

Also, as a bonus for you in this book, you will find a code that gives you access to download 6 meditations for free that are retailed at £60.

Mindfulness is a mystery to most yet thousands of studies have shown how it can easily combat stress, anxiety and depression.

This self-help book shows you the proof and then step-by-step teaches you the methods that are easy to follow for a more fulfilled, calmer, happier, more peaceful life.

Enjoy this journey in helping yourself create a more positive life for yourself and take your time with each technique, it is not a race, all that is important is with each new day you take yourself forward and learn to have the life that you deserve to have.

ABOUT THE AUTHOR

Tamsin Cooper is an International Master Hypnotherapist who has dedicated over twenty years in her professional career helping thousands of clients to overcome anxiety and stress and achieve a happier, calmer, more peaceful life for themselves.

You can watch real life video testimonials from some of her clients on her YouTube channel Tamsin Cooper Hypnotherapy or by visiting her website www.tamsincooper.co.uk

Table of Contents

CHAPTER ONE

YOUR FIRST STEPS TOWARDS

SELF-HEALING

HOW TO REDUCE STRESS AND ANXIETY

LEARN HOW TO OVERCOME STRESS, WORRY, ANXIETY AND OVERTHINKING.

REGAIN YOUR SELF-CONFIDENCE BY CONTROLLING THE ENEMY WITHIN, FOR A HAPPIER AND MORE PEACEFUL LIFE.

When you feel trapped in your own desolation and despair, like a caged bird frantically beating it's wings against the bars, all that is necessary for your release is a prayer. Send out your heartfelt plea for help and a hand will come and open the door of your cage. You will fly free and unharmed and will sing joyously again.

Little Owl Cards 2

It is a sad fact that with the changing times more and more people are seen to be suffering from stress and anxiety. This book will help you to counter the effects of increasing stress levels.

But the million-dollar question is what makes this book different in comparison to all the other stress and anxiety self-help books out there? In all honesty, I really cannot answer that it is for you, the reader to decide; to me, as an author, all that matters is that you, as a reader can resonate with my thoughts and ideas. My sole purpose for writing this book is to help you by giving you a huge variance of tools, exercises, affirmations and meditations that you can implement into your life immediately.

If at any point while reading, you do feel that this book isn't for you and that you must continue your journey for answers elsewhere, just flick through the exercises and choose one self-help exercise that you find easy to include in your life. Trust me, even that one chunk of positivity can bring about a wonderful change in your life.

I have written this book after personally battling with anxiety for years. I didn't know at the time how to help myself and overcome the ordeal so I kept on enduring the pain quietly. There were times when I felt that I was running in a circle, trying to flee from the 'black dog' but continuously failing and falling back into the pit of depression. I have learned so much. This book will help you to cope and, at the same time create a sense of wellbeing.

It is said that life is a journey and every journey has a story. We are all on a journey and we all have a story, this is mine.

Where to start? For a long time, I lived under the black cloud of anxiety and led an extremely stressful life. I was in an unhappy marriage and it took me years to eventually pluck up the courage to leave. The day I left, I had not only become a divorced woman but also a single parent to two small children. From then onwards every day was a battle to survive. At times, I used to feel that I wouldn't be able to cope. All I wanted was to somehow move forward and yet, all the time it seemed as though I was stepping back. Waking up every morning with a heart that constantly tried to hammer itself out of my chest and a constant feeling of foreboding that something terrible was going to happen had become a norm. From the moment I used to wake up till the instant I fell asleep, there was a constant fight, a fight against myself. A negative chatterbox inside my head, slowly sucking out the positivity and happiness from my life was the 'enemy within'. I felt that I had no peace in my life, I felt devoid of peace and joy. I felt empty.

This was my life for far too many years, and this is the very reason that compelled me to write this book. No matter how you are feeling right now, as you work your way through this book, you will find an abundance of ways to discipline and master your negative thoughts and emotions. You will begin to feel lighter and happier, you will learn to live rather than just surviving.

This book has been created by keeping my own struggles in mind, and also that of the many thousands of clients I have helped. It is a success template which I have carefully put together, I am hopeful that as you start to read and go deeper, you will find ways to deal with the brutalities of life and emerge as a happier, calmer, and a more positive person. Not only that, you will gradually start enjoying a better state of emotional and mental wellbeing.

Life is all about experience and joy and I have written this book with the belief that it will enable you to experience a new sense of freedom. You are your own Master and I sincerely wish that you learn how to enjoy life, waking up each morning with a feeling of excitement and faith that you will find a way, no matter what challenges you are confronted with. You alone can deal with the monster trying to eat you up from the inside. As your mind learns how to get rid of the negativity, you will begin to realise your true potential and transform from a chrysalis into a beautiful butterfly that is ready to spread its wings and fly.

> *"Come to the edge," he said.*
> *"We can't, we're afraid!" they responded.*
> *"Come to the edge," he said.*
> *"We can't, we will fall!" they responded.*
> *"Come to the edge," he said.*
> *And so they came.*
> *And he pushed them.*
> *And they flew.*
> *Guillaume Apollinaire*

I have been a Master Clinical Hypnotherapist for over twenty years specializing in working with stress and anxiety. I am very passionate about my work and this book is a combination of my professional training and my own self-help tools that I used to overcome my mental issues and that of my clients.

Case Study

Alan is in his late twenties.

From the outside, he would seem to have the perfect life with a successful career, a lovely home, and a beautiful and supportive partner, and yet, on Alan's consultation, I learned that he had been signed off work with anxiety. He had suffered from anxiety for 12 years and had had a breakdown. He was no longer able to focus on his work. His home had become his 'safe place' and he would only ever venture out if his partner was with him. He had also developed social anxiety. He said that he felt 'disconnected' and 'didn't feel like himself'. He felt no joy, no fulfillment in life and worried constantly. He couldn't sleep and would lie in bed for hours, tossing and turning until he would asleep, exhausted. He also kept waking during the night panicked and worried about the previous day and also what tomorrow might/would bring. He would break down in tears as anxiety and worry overwhelmed him. Not knowing which way to turn, he looked up a professional therapist on Google and found my name.

I immediately began treating Alan with my Stress Management Programme and included some of the very same exercises that you will find in this book.

On Alan's second session with me, he reported that he had more energy, felt more positive, much calmer and relaxed.

On His third session, he reported that he had more get-up-and-go, his sleep had greatly improved, he could fall asleep easily and would only wake up once during the night rather than three or four times. His social anxiety was also lessening. He felt that he was becoming more sociable and was able to communicate with others easily.

On his fourth session, it was lovely to see the spark in his eyes and to see him smiling and laughing. I could clearly see a completely different 'Alan' compared to the man that I had first met during his initial consultation. He reported that his anxiety was gone and he felt much more positive and confident and had been looking forward to returning to work.

The reason behind narrating Alan's story is to reassure you that your life can be different too. You too can change, just like Alan.

The Human mind has on average 55,000 – 85,000 thoughts a day and most of these can potentially be negative thoughts. I'm going to help you focus more on calmer thoughts, more positive thoughts.

The good news is that if you follow the exercises in this book that thousands of my clients have learnt to use and put into practice then you will experience a change as well quickly or gradually. By controlling the enemy within, you can live the life that you deserve – a happier and a more peaceful life.

FIRST TASK

In the morning, before getting out of bed and allowing the first thoughts of the day to come flooding into your mind, stop for a while and think about three things that you can be grateful for. In case you can't think of any, go right to the basics, for example, 'I'm grateful for the fact that I have 10 fingers and toes',' I'm grateful for the fact that my lungs are clear and that I can breathe', 'I'm grateful for the cup of coffee that I will be drinking when I go into the kitchen', 'I'm grateful that the sun is shining today', 'I'm grateful for the roof over my head', 'I'm grateful for..' and so on.

Similarly, when you go to bed at night, repeat the 'I am grateful for' exercise. Again, you might have to stay at the basics 'I'm grateful for the fact that I didn't have a panic attack today', 'I'm grateful for the dinner that I ate tonight and that I have a full belly', 'I'm grateful for the television that I can watch my favourite series on'.

If you put this task into practice every day, as soon as you wake up, and while you lie in your bed at night before going to sleep, you will begin to find the task becoming easier. Not only will you be able to find more and more things to be grateful for but you will also begin to feel the change coming about quite naturally. Your mind will learn to focus on more positive thoughts than bad thoughts, things like 'I'm grateful that I felt like smiling today and so I did', 'I'm grateful for my lovely soft, warm and welcoming bed', 'I'm grateful for this wonderful day' and the list goes on.

Through the chapters, you will also learn how to break the habit of overthinking. You will be able to control the enemy within, feeling more confident and more in control of your life and most importantly, your own self. This book will help you deal with those uncomfortable thoughts and feelings that destroy your inner comfort and peace. You may feel that your circumstances are the same but the way you deal with them has changed. You will be able to deal with the stress more calmly and be more focussed. Hence, your levels of stress and anxiety will reduce.

This book is packed with many life-changing coping mechanisms, strategies, and meditations to help you to deal with life's issues. It will not only help you overcome stress, anxiety and social anxiety but you will also be able to regain your confidence and start feeling good about yourself. You will become more optimistic and a more peaceful and happier version of yourself. And remember, a happier 'You' means a happier life. Additionally, this book will also help you deal with the 'what-ifs' that plague your mind and give birth to feelings of self-doubt.

Here are a few short testimonials from clients:

"I really wasn't in a good place. Nothing in my life seemed to be going right. I felt emotional all the time. I felt very low and my confidence levels were zero. Everything was affected by how I felt, my work, my family, my life. Tamsin helped me to get my self-worth back and also helped me to feel positive and begin to have the confidence to live life again."

"My thoughts were mainly to do with worrying, thinking badly about myself, like, I just wasn't good enough, constantly putting myself down and I always had this knot in my stomach that something bad was going to happen. Tamsin helped me so much and I am very grateful, I actually feel lighter and have learned to be so much more relaxed and happier in myself."

" I suffered from anxiety and panic attacks, they were so bad that I couldn't leave my flat, Tamsin has helped me to get my life back, a big THANK YOU!"

And another short testimonial:

"I retrained on a professional level, the training was extremely stressful, and it had impacted my personal life. Tamsin helped me to focus and remain calm and to stop being such a 'stress head', brilliant, thanks Tamsin."

By visiting my website www.tamsincooper.co.uk you can see actual video testimonials from ordinary people, just like you, who have benefitted from my help.

More video testimonials can be found on my YouTube channel 'Tamsin Cooper Hypnotherapy'.

As you turn the pages in this book I hope you enjoy reading and using the self-help tools in this book as much as I have enjoyed writing this book for you.

CHAPTER TWO

BERYL-THE ENEMY WITHIN

"Oh my dear, your sorrows we employ to teach you how to live your life, to bring you greater joy. If it were all smooth plain sailing, then nothing would be learned, For we have greater things in mind, rewards you will have earned."

Little Owl Cards 2

When negative thoughts start to run free in your mind, you, unconsciously, condition your body to accept this thought- process as your 'normal'. In short, you're hardwiring your brain to accept these pessimistic feelings as your 'reality'.

Sometimes, you spend so much time worrying about all the 'what if's' in life that you start living in constant fear and forget to 'live' life altogether. Every time you worry, you're releasing stress hormones into your body. These stress hormones have the ability to take over and shut down the immune system, either partially or completely.

The good news is: You may be powerless in controlling the stressful circumstances in your life but you are not powerless in learning how to control the emotions resulting from stress.

BERYL

As I sit here writing this book, I am trying to recall the very first time when I met Beryl. I feel that I have always known Beryl, she seems so familiar as though she is a part of me.

Ever since I was a child, Beryl has enjoyed whispering and sometimes shouting horrible things at me. She has stayed with me through my teenage years and into my adulthood. Sometimes her constant barrage would make me feel so low, so very low. At times, I would think that I was going mad. The truth is that I wasn't, I was just anxious and depressed. It's just how she 'made' me feel on so many occasions.

Beryl has made me doubt myself, take antidepressants and withdraw socially from the world. I also managed to get myself into all kinds of financial pickles as somehow, spending money made me feel happier and more in control.

Let me ask you a question: if you had a friend who constantly criticises you or puts you down, what would you do? I hope that you would tell that 'friend' to get lost. So why didn't I tell Beryl to take a hike? I couldn't! Because Beryl resides within me; she is a part of me, she is my **inner voice**.

For many years, I had this inner voice inside my head that constantly put me down and made me question my self-worth. I used to think that if I told anyone about 'Beryl', they would have me sectioned. So I continued to believe everything that she said about me. As I allowed her to run riot inside my head, her words started to mirror my life and ultimately, I became what I believed.

When did I first meet Beryl? Was it when I was told that the world didn't revolve around me? Was it when my Nan told me that I would never be pretty? Was it when I asked for something and I was told that money doesn't grow on trees? Was it when I used to cry and was told to stop crying or I would be given something to cry about?

As an adult, after many years of self-work, I realised that my world does revolve around me. I am indeed the most important person in my world. This is not said from a selfish point of view, rather from a place of self-love and self-preservation. You can be good and kind and thoughtful to other people while holding yourself in high regard. Finally, I realised that everyone has a Beryl.

Beryl, define beauty? What is beauty? Is it what we see when we look at an airbrushed model? That's exactly what I believed! Do you have moments when you tell yourself: 'I'm too fat, I'm too thin, I'm too old, I'm too ugly'?

Different cultures around the world have a different perspective on beauty. But do you know what 'real' beauty is? It is **You**. You are a unique, special and beautiful being and now is the time for you to embrace your imperfect self because you are 'perfect', just the way you are. And who said that you can't have what you want? On a lighter note, money is made from paper and paper does come from trees so technically, money indeed grows on trees!

Throughout this book, I show you how to deal with your inner voice with tasks, exercises, meditations and affirmations that you can straight away put into practice to regain control over your 'Beryl'. Do you know what I do when Beryl tries to criticise me? I simply tell her to belt up! I've got better things to do with my day than listen to her!

Just before Christmas, I travelled to London to watch a Christmas pantomime. On the Tube and also whilst walking through the West End, I noticed that no one was smiling. There was just this uniformed fixed stare on everyone's face. I nudged my partner and said, 'look at their eyes'! I noticed every pair of eyes was devoid of life. There was no flicker of joy or the Christmas spirit, everyone was just hurrying along. I found this incredibly sad as it was Christmas Eve. I wondered how many of those poor souls were 'listening' to their Beryls.

I believe that the eyes are the windows to the soul and in all my years of practice in hypnotherapy, I have seen many clients come to me with the same glazed look.

Nothing gives me greater pleasure than witnessing that 'spark' reigniting in their eyes, as they begin to change over the weeks that we work together.

I have helped thousands of clients over the years to achieve a life that perhaps they could only dream of. I feel very humbled to say that I played a part in making their dreams come true. I have developed a system over many years, not only inspired by my personal experiences but also from my clients' journeys. It is both an honour and a privilege to be entrusted to walk by someone, hold their hand briefly along a part of their life's path and know that I have made a difference.

This book is dedicated to YOU. You deserve a good life, as we all do. It's time to put your Beryl firmly in her/his place and start living a wonderful life.

Before I move further, let me give you a suggestion. If you haven't read the book or seen the film called 'The Secret', I suggest you make this one of your to-do tasks. 'The Secret' explains The Law of Attraction.

The Law of Attraction is a Universal Law and is based on the concept, 'what you send out, you will receive'. I always use a boomerang as the easiest way to explain this: You throw the boomerang out and it comes back to you. You throw it out again, it comes back again. Think of yourself as a boomerang or a human magnet, what you think or feel is drawn to you, and it then becomes your reality. Think about good things and good things will happen. Your energy will begin to change and you will attract only good things into your life. On the other hand, with negative and stressful thoughts, the stress will continue.

Perhaps you have spent a long time listening to your 'Beryl' and that's ok, you knew no different then but now it's time to control your 'Beryl', for good.

CASE STUDY

Diane came to me, suffering from anxiety. She had tried CBT but it hadn't helped. She was prone to panic attacks and worried constantly. Her home was her sanctuary and safe place. She hardly ever ventured out and had isolated herself from friends and family. She hated to even think of being in a crowded place. Her thoughts were negative, her confidence was in tatters and she feared not only for her health but for her loved ones' health too. She described herself as being 'trapped' inside, hating how she felt but had given up hope of ever feeling 'normal' again. Eating was also a problem as comfort-eating had become a daily habit, snacking constantly in between meals and consequently piling the weight on. There were no distinctive triggers to the reason as to why she felt like this, it had simply gotten worse over the years. She felt that she was struggling against her mind all the time (Beryl).

Diane also had a fear of flying, quite unfortunate as she lived in the UK and her family lived in Spain.

During her first session, I explained how she was being controlled by her negative Beryl. I formulated a detailed and personalised therapy plan that also included some of the exercises in this book including the weight loss therapy that you can find in Chapter Nine of this book.

After her first hypnosis session with me, Diane reported that she had begun to feel some relief and was beginning to feel a little bit more confident in herself.

After her second session, she was beginning to 'think' differently (starting to control Beryl) and had left her home a few times, once to go to the cinema! She was following the weight loss therapy religiously too!

After her third session, Diane was happily eating just three meals a day and had even lost some weight. She no longer felt anxious and the anxiety around her health was virtually zero. She no longer focussed on the bad feelings and thoughts. Instead, whenever she felt uneasy, she followed some of the exercises in this book and remained present until the feeling had subsided.

After her fourth session, Diane reported how much happier and how much more in control she felt. She was able to leave the house and had taken a part-time job, even making some friends at her new workplace, AND had booked a flight to visit her family in Spain.

Dr. Masaru Emoto claimed that human consciousness could affect the molecular structure of water. Emoto wrote a book that was published in 2004, called 'The Hidden Messages in Water'. It became a New York Times bestseller.

The basis of the book was an experiment with water. He simply said words to a drop of water, crystalized the drop, then took a photograph after that. Emoto used negative words such as hate, pain, and positive words such as love, happiness.

The results were amazing:

The drops of water had responded to the words, the negative words produced crystal shapes that were ugly and misformed. The positive words produced crystals of breathtaking beauty, beautifully shaped geometric formations.

He also claimed that polluted water could be 'healed' through the frequency of positive thoughts, words, even music or sound of a certain frequency.

Perhaps you are wondering how self-healing is related to Dr. Masaru Emoto and his experiment? The average adult human body is 60% water. So, if the human mind has about 55,000 to 85,000 thoughts a day on average while the majority of those thoughts are being dominated by Beryl (negative thoughts), what impact do you think that is having on your body?

If you have never seen Emoto's work before, check out photographs of his work on the internet, you may be shocked by what you see. I was shocked too and for me, it was a huge wakeup call.

Try to be mindful of your thoughts and actions and every time you drink water, say 'I love you'. You can also repeat this with your food as most foods hold a high water content. While cooking, say 'I love you' to the food and while eating, say 'thank you' for the nourishment.

You could even go one step further. When you are with other people, say 'I love you' to that person in your mind so they absorb the positive vibes and have the opportunity to thrive and heal too.

Can you imagine if this becomes a daily practice in your life, how would the water inside your body be affected? How will you be affected? How much happier, calmer and healthier you can become!

TASK 2

The 321 Emotional Reset Technique – Dr. Richard Nongard

This is a fast and effective exercise to try when you are feeling stressed, worried and anxious. It'll also help you if you feel that you lack self-confidence.

Count your next three breaths. You don't need to breathe in any special way, just count out your breaths. This helps you focus on the moment, this very moment. It also helps you to ground yourself.

Next, take both of your hands and put them on your shoulders, hug yourself, hold yourself tightly, this releases oxytocin, a feel-good hormone.

Now, close your eyes and take one minute to be totally in the present, this is called mindfulness. Set aside all your worries, stresses, anxieties, problems, all the what if's, the regrets, the could have's, the should have's. Do not worry about the future, just stay fully present in the moment.

Pay attention to your breathing. Focus on the chair beneath you or the floor, if you are standing. Tell yourself that the only time we have is this moment. Yesterday is history, tomorrow is a mystery, all we have is the present and that is why it's a gift. Spend that one minute in silence, one minute being present.

Open your eyes, put a smile on your face and feel fantastic!

CHAPTER THREE

A LESSON IN KINDNESS

Are you flying in the face of your destiny? Are you doing what your inner senses are prodding you to do? Think harder. Stop and take stock. Look ahead to possible consequences. Then you will be able to go ahead or change direction according to your true feelings. Your inner feelings know what is right for you, personally.

Little Owl Cards 2

There has been much study on establishing links between kindness and happiness. Showing kindness can help you feel better, calmer, stronger and less depressed.

A study led by Dr. Oliver Scott Curry from the Institute of Cognitive and Evolutionary Anthropology at the University of Oxford stated that human beings are social creatures and they happily help family, friends, colleagues, community members and even strangers under some conditions.

Dr. Curry's study was commissioned by kindness.org, a US-based nonprofit organization and was funded by an anonymous donor. Dr. Curry, Director of The Oxford Morals Project studies the psychology of moral values and how morality varies around the world.

His research suggests that people do derive satisfaction from helping others. He goes onto say that we genuinely care about others' welfare and random acts of kindness are a good way of making new friends and kickstarting supportive social relationships. He concludes by saying that acts of kindness will not change our lives but might nudge us in the right direction.

How does being kind benefit you? It lifts your mood, for example, say that you are driving to work and the traffic is heavy and a random stranger lets you out of a junction, how does that make you feel? When someone shows you an act of kindness, you are more likely to show kindness to someone else that day. Perhaps someone else stuck in that traffic. In turn, that someone that you have shown kindness to will probably be kind to someone else. A ripple effect of kindness from just one person can positively affect so many other people; it's like a chain reaction.

Let me share a personal experience with you.

When I had offices for my hypnotherapy practice, I used to stop off on the way to work to buy lunch from the local supermarket. Often, there used to be a homeless person, sitting outside the shop's entrance. So many people just walked past him, as though he was invisible.

The first time I saw him, I asked if he needed anything as I was going into the shop anyway. He replied that he would like some food and a drink. I bought him a sandwich, hot chicken, some milk, and some wipes to clean his hands. He was so grateful, so humbled.

The second time I saw him was on a bitterly cold day. I felt frozen just walking the short distance from my car to the shop. Goodness knows how cold that poor man was! I asked him if I could get him some clothing and he asked for a clean pair of underpants. I bought him a multipack of underwear, a thick scarf, a jumper and some thermal vests. He was over the moon.

I asked him how long he had been sitting outside the shop that morning. He replied that he had been there for three hours. We got talking and he told me his story. He had been made redundant and as a result, he couldn't pay the mortgage. The home was repossessed, his wife left him and refused to let him see his children. Eventually, he was left with no money and found himself homeless and started living on the street.

It is said that we are only ever three paychecks away from becoming homeless. 'There but for the grace of God go I' is the saying that comes into my head as I write this.

His name is John. I gave him £10 to go and buy himself a coffee from the local coffee shop. To my surprise, he told me that the staff in the coffee shop had barred him and wouldn't let him in as he was so scruffy. I persuaded him to go and that I would stay with him. We went into the coffee shop. I was meticulously dressed in a suit and an expensive tailored coat and was greeted by smiles from the staff member at the counter. John stood behind me, I asked for two coffees and a hot breakfast and requested the girl brought them over to the table for my friend and I. I, then acknowledged John and said 'this is my friend, I am sure you will make him feel as welcome as you have made me feel'. The girl blushed and no more was said. John enjoyed his breakfast and coffee.

As we sat there, I gave him some self-help tools that you can also find in this book. Shortly afterward, it was time for me to leave for the office but I promised John that I would contact a friend that helped homeless people get off the streets. I went into the office, called my friend and asked him to help John.

I haven't seen John again but I hear reports that he is doing ok. Sometimes, you can lose your way through circumstances that are beyond your control but a simple act of kindness from someone can make a huge difference.

Every day, I strive to be kind to at least one person. This way, I extend that kindness out to everyone that I meet throughout my day. This makes me feel that my life is worthwhile and gives me such joy. However, I admit that for me, this is relatively easy as it is also my profession to help my clients make positive changes in their lives.

As I look back to that day when I went to the coffee shop with John, I feel positive that the staff member that served us also received a lesson of kindness and compassion towards others. I hope that she showed an act of kindness to someone else that day and created her ripple effect of kindness.

No matter who you are, everyone is affected by kindness. You can be having the absolute worst day but if someone shows kindness to you, it instantly makes you feel good. For that moment, you forget about your awful day as you become touched by that act of kindness. Who knows, that might improve the rest of your day!

Even small gestures such as smiling at another person can have an impact. Maybe that person you smiled at was feeling low and having a bad day. By smiling at him it could change his mood, make him feel happier and he is more likely to pass that happiness onto another person.

Case Study

When I first met Mark, he was suffering from stress, anxiety, PTSD and had suicidal thoughts. He had been in the army for a great many years and was finding it very difficult to adjust to civilian life. He found solace in alcohol and drugs.

His marriage was on the rocks; his wife was threatening to leave him unless he sought help. He had tried counselling but it had not helped him. His stress levels were high and he was very anxious. He always felt on edge, was super sensitive to noise and had a short fuse. Almost everything made him erupt. When I asked him how he felt inside, he said that he just felt empty. For him, each day was a struggle and he restlessly waited for the afternoon when he could habitually drink and take drugs. Although he knew his marriage was in serious trouble, he had no idea how to get his happy marital life back again.

We spoke about who the 'ideal Mark' was and at my request, Mark wrote out a list. The usual things were on the list that clients often write: to be calmer, more positive, to not let things get to me, to not get so worked up, to be stress-free, to be happy, to be drug-free, to be healthy, to drink in moderation, not to feel overwhelmed. It was a good list and I congratulated Mark on being so honest.

I then broached the subject of adding a few more things to the list: to be more loving, to be more caring. To this, he looked at me with a blank expression.

I spoke about his marriage and asked if he wanted to work on it. 'Of course, I want to', he snapped. I replied, 'then the first step is to show small acts of kindness'. I gave Mark a sheet of paper and asked him to go home and write 10 things that he could think of, where he could show kindness. At least four of those should include his marriage.

On Mark's second session, the light had been switched on in his eyes. He seemed so much happier. He had moderated alcohol down to three nights a week, instead of seven days a week and hadn't touched drugs. He had bought his wife some chocolates and a bunch of flowers and had asked her if they could try to save the marriage. Being a woman, I felt so happy for him and suggested he buy the biggest bouquet of flowers for his wife and have them delivered to her. I also asked him to make a reservation for two in a nice restaurant. Mark admitted that he would never have thought of doing that in a million years!

On Mark's third session, he told me that his wife had cried when the bouquet was delivered. The tears were tears of happiness. They had also gone out for dinner and had had a wonderful night. He even surprised me and said that he had bought his wife an expensive bottle of perfume that she used to wear years ago but was unable to afford to buy. He reported that he was feeling so much calmer, happier and noises no longer bothered him. He seemed so much more hopeful and happier. He felt the urge to 'live' life and kept on adding more and more things to the list.

On Mark's fourth session, he reported that his wife was doing little random acts of kindness for him and that their relationship had rekindled. My heart swelled with happiness for him. Mark was now feeling really good, hadn't touched drugs for weeks and was only drinking moderately on a Friday and a Saturday night. He had also reconnected with a couple of old friends and had begun to have a social life.

I spoke to Mark three months after his fourth session. Life was good, his anti-anxiety medication had been reduced. He had been offered a promotion at work and felt confident enough to accept the new role. His marriage was good. He was calmer, more patient, more relaxed and was able to let go of stuff. His PTSD had disappeared and he was feeling amazing.

Well done Mark, I am so proud of you.

Task three

Write as many ways as you can imagine how you can be kind to others. If you're unable to think of more than one or two ways, you can always come back to this list at a later date. At some point, you will begin to feel that the more you show kindness, the more you will **want** to show kindness.

1_____

2_____

3_____

4_____

5_____

6_____

7_____

8_____

9_____

10_____

CHAPTER FOUR

MINDFULNESS EXERCISES: PART ONE

When you are in doubt as to what action to take, sit down and reflect on the situation. Contemplate what has been and what could be. Hold before you your wildest dreams and see what can be done to bring those into reality. In short, put your mind to the question. In these quiet reflections will come the knowledge from your innermost being.

Little Owl Cards 2

In this chapter, there are 15 exercises to help you deal with stress, anxiety, over worrying and pain management.

THE EXERCISES

1. The power of breath and deep breathing is highly underestimated. We tend to breathe too shallow or high up in our chests especially when we are feeling stressed or nervous. Just take a few seconds during the day to breathe down into your stomach. Try 5 or 6 of these breaths and at the same time, try to

breathe as slowly as you can. It not only helps to calm you but also sends more oxygen to your brain, helping you to think more clearly and reducing that 'brain fog'.

2. Sometimes, we can feel our strength ebbing away from us. It could be due to a traumatic event or circumstances in life pulling us down. An easy and quick way to get your strength back is to sit on an upright chair, perhaps your kitchen chair or if you are sitting on your sofa prop yourself up with some cushions. Imagine that your spine is made of steel. Imagine that stress or anxiety has depleted you and chipped away chunks out of the steel. As you sit there, imagine that steel reshaping itself and filling in all of the chips. Imagine those gaps being filled and the chips being regenerated one by one, or all at once. You may even experience and feel your back wanting to straighten as you imagine doing this. Now see that rod of steel absolutely perfect, smooth and shiny, as good as new.

3. When we feel under the weather or unwell, it can heighten our stress levels. Similarly, it can increase the aches, pains and headaches. As we try to get on with our daily lives, that pain can keep edging in and make us think about it constantly. This can make us feel grumpy, irritable and stressed.

    The human mind is incredible. Did you know that what we think we become? Wouldn't it be nice to be able to imagine something and it happens? Well, the good news is that you can do this by using the power of your mind.

So I want you to use your imagination to scan your body and locate the pain. Where is that pain? Have you found it?

Now I want you to give it a colour. Red is a good colour to use as we tend to associate red with anger, danger, pain, inflammation. You can also choose your own colour, the choice is yours.

Now I want you to imagine zapping that colour out. You can really crank up your imagination here. Imagine using a laser gun or a laser beam or something else, it is entirely your choice. Pale that colour out until you are left with a soft pink or white.

4. Pretend to take a shot of medicine every day. You can imagine the medicine as a pill for convenience or out of an imaginary medicine bottle. This medication fulfils your every need and will soothe you and heal the pain, making you feel better, and at the same time giving you an incredible feeling of wellbeing.

5. Another good mental exercise for pain management is to locate the pain, once again. Where is the pain in your body?

Now imagine that part of your body filled with lots of black spots or dots. Can you see them all covering the pain? Those black spots? Now imagine that you have a laser gun, perhaps like a laser gun in a science fiction movie.

Start shooting at those spots, those dark spots. Shoot them as fast as you can, every single one of them until you have gotten rid of them all.

Make a game of it, some of those stubborn spots may try to come back. Imagine that they're not finished with you yet. They want to give you pain. They are so used to giving you pain that they don't want to give up, they do not like change.

Say to yourself, 'really? Who's the Boss here? Who's the one in charge of the gun?'

Shoot them, get them, shoot them all.

6. How about reducing that pain down? Locate the pain. Now give it a shape; the first shape that comes into your mind will be the right shape for you. It could be a square, a circle, a rectangle or a spikey shape.

    Now take that shape and imagine shrinking it down to the size of a pinhead.

    Now shrink that pinhead down to the size of a tiny dot. As you look at that tiny small dot, I want you to shrink that dot down even more until there is absolutely nothing left.

7. Have you ever stood beneath a waterfall? I wonder how it would feel? I want you to imagine inside your mind a magical waterfall. Imagine standing underneath the waterfall. The water is warm, welcoming, pleasant, and you feel perfectly safe. The ledge on which you are standing is wide. As those droplets of water softly cascade over your body, each one is caught in the sunlight, reflecting the colours of the rainbow. The droplets resemble glistening jewels, they are beautiful and exquisite. They feel warm and your body and skin welcome them. As the

water flows over you, you look down and see a mud-coloured liquid beneath your feet. You wonder where this is coming from as you are sure it wasn't there before. It takes a few seconds for you to realise that the dark colour liquid is coming directly from you. This is all the negativity that you have held inside you. The magical waterfall is cleansing you and removing all of that toxic stuff from inside you. You begin to feel a sense of wellbeing.

Now you begin to smile to yourself. As you look down again, you notice that the water is now running clear. You feel great! Cleansed and wonderfully energised!

8. Take a balloon and when you're ready, take a really big deep breath. Now blow all of your frustration, anger, worry and stress into that balloon. Keep doing this until you feel calm.

9. Clear all of that negativity out of your mind. Imagine a hot summer day and you find yourself standing at the base of a mountain. As you look up, you realise that there is a part of you that is feeling compelled to climb the mountain. You don't know the reason, all you know is that you want to climb it.

The mountain represents the uphill struggles in your life. You begin to climb the mountain but after a short while, your legs begin to ache. You are now finding it harder to breathe as the higher you climb, the air starts to become thinner. Imagine that journey up the mountain. What do you see? What can you hear? What is that negative chatterbox inside your head saying to you? Do you want to give up and find your way back down the mountain without getting to the top? You have started, so why not finish the climb? You decide to continue the climb. Eventually, you reach the top of the mountain and find a soft patch of grass to sit on and rest for a while. You begin to think about how stressful your life is, how things are turning out and how unhappy you are. Allow that stress and frustration to build up inside you.

Now I want you to imagine getting up and standing on the top of the mountain. Take the biggest breath that you can muster. On your breath out, I want you to imagine shouting and screaming the frustration and stress out of your body, out of your lungs. Just let it all out. Repeat this three times.

10. Imagine a positive person. This could be someone that you know in your life or someone that you have read about or seen in a movie or a television programme. Someone you would wish to be like. Now imagine sitting opposite that person and telling them all of your problems. Imagine what that person would say to you, how they would advise you and how they would spin your thoughts around to positive thoughts. Imagine if that person was living your life, how they would remove all the negative aspects and replace it all with positive thoughts and solutions.

11. Pretend to love life. You will be pleasantly surprised at how quickly you begin to start to believe this to be real. As you pretend to love living your life, you will begin to change for the better.

12. Imagine a clear night sky, not a cloud to be seen, filled with a thousand stars. You find yourself sitting and resting in a place of beauty. Perhaps at a beach or the edge of a wood or a calm lake. As you look up at the stars and feel a cool night breeze on your face, you begin to wonder about the significance of everything that you perceive as your reality. How many thousands of miles away are each one of those stars and how small we are, each one of us in the grand scheme of the universe. Begin to think about your problems and your troubles. When you look up at that night sky, you will know that whatever life has seemingly thrown at you, it is so insignificant compared to the universe. Those stars will still be shining there in a thousand years and that makes you realise how short a lifetime really is. Make a vow to yourself that you will now begin to make a difference in your life. It may mean that the first steps that you take are tiny baby steps. Remember that each step you take will bring a new brighter and happier future for you, slowly but surely.

13. Imagine yourself on a tropical beach and you are lying comfortably in a hammock. Your body is totally supported and you feel very safe. The hammock sways ever so slightly in the gentlest of breezes. You can imagine feeling the warmth of the sun on your skin. As you imagine laying there with your eyes closed, you begin to experience a feeling of wellbeing. Begin to think about all of the good things in your life. It could be your family, friends, health, partner, having a roof over your head, food in your cupboards. It could be anything, no matter how small or insignificant it may be. As you continue

to imagine yourself in the hammock, think of ten things that you are grateful for. As you think of those things, smile to yourself and feel thankful.

14. Imagine that your life has come to a crossroads. There are two paths before you: the first path is the one that you are familiar with. It is a continuation of your life and everything that you already are and have experienced so far. Whereas, the other path seems unfamiliar, but brighter and shinier. As you look at the two paths, the familiar one feels safe as this is the path that you know while the other path, the shinier path holds your curiosity. Do you feel brave enough to venture onto the brighter path? All it will take is just one step.

15. Make a Happy Board. You can either make this on your phone or you can physically use a notice board or a corkboard. Fill it with all the things that you would like in your life that you think would make you happy. The sky is the limit, no barriers, no financial limitations. Just dream of all those lovely things that you would like to happen in your life. If you want more money, be very specific about the amount. A house, what kind of house? Try to find a picture of your ideal house or describe in words what your ideal house would look like. How many rooms? Does it have a garden?

A holiday, where would you like to go? A car, what make, what colour? A relationship, make a long list of everything that you would prefer in your ideal partner including looks, personality and so on. Again, be very specific.

I learned the hard way with the relationship part. I described my ideal man on my happy board: how he looked, how tall he was and he came into my life less than a week later. Appearance-wise, he was everything that I had asked for, even down to a specific tattoo that I had described that I wanted him to have. Unfortunately, I hadn't been specific enough about his character traits and personality. So my advice to you is: be very specific.

I make a new happy board every year and keep it in my bedroom. I look at it now and again and smile to myself when so many of the things that I have placed on there happen and come true.

CHAPTER FIVE

MINDFULNESS EXERCISES : PART TWO

*All of the irritants of your day are not remembered in the latter
years of your life, so why give them importance now? Deal with
them for what they are — nothings. In this way, you will be calm
and meet all things and your life will be tranquil.*

Little Owl Cards 2

Here are fifteen more exercises to help you live a happier
life.

1. Imagine yourself walking along a beautiful beach,
    just by the water's edge. How does the soft, wet,
    smooth sand feel between your toes? Does it feel
    warm or cool? You look up at the sky, is the sun
    beginning to rise or, is it beginning to set? The choice
    is yours.

    You marvel at the array of colours now beginning to
    fill the sky: reds, oranges, mauves, yellows, blues,
    golds. Perhaps you can hear the sound of the gulls
    and the waves gently lapping onto the shore, softly

caressing your feet. The air is comforting and warm against your skin.

You let out a soft sigh of contentment, you feel so calm and so peaceful. Now and again, you see a shell and you bend down to pick it up. Each shell has a word written upon it. You look at the words: positivity, health, happiness, calmness. Think of all the positive words that you would like to see on the shells washing up on the shore of your life. The shells with those words imprinted on them that mean the most to you. You have permission to gather them up and put them in your pocket so that you can keep them close to you.

Every now and again, you can pull out a shell and read what's written on it, it will bring that positive energy into your life that the word represents.

2. Appreciate each day and look for nice moments throughout your day. Those moments may appear to be small but they are there. It could be a stranger opening a door for you, finding a coin on the pavement/sidewalk, someone wishing you a great day and meaning it, a stranger letting you go in front of them in a queue, receiving a hug, someone smiling at you, someone paying you a compliment. It is ok for you to accept a compliment. Or having a conversation that makes you feel good. Now think and reflect on your day and recall the nice moments and as you remember them, smile.

3. Be kind to yourself. Instead of finding yourself worrying about what you haven't managed to get done, think about the one or two things that you

have accomplished. Be proud of yourself for having done that.

4. Imagine paying your bills easily every month; imagine your bank account statement with an extra zero on the end. Feel the accomplishment of managing your bills and having some monies left over for something nice.

5. Do something kind for someone else today. It's even better when you do a random act of kindness for a stranger, someone that you don't know and expect absolutely nothing back in return.

6. Let's play a game of pretend. Remember how you used to pretend and imagine as a child? Those games of make-believe?

    Imagine someone that you know is confident. It could be someone that you have read about in a book or seen on the television or in a movie or someone that you know in real life. This person could be male or female, it doesn't matter. Now imagine being that person. What would it feel like to be them? How would they talk? How would they think? How would they stand, back and shoulders straight? Now imagine copying them and mimicking them in every single way that you can think of. Pretend to be that person and imagine how they would react to your problems, stresses, worries and anxieties.

7. Think of one thing that you are good at. Remember we can't all be good at everything. So when you think about someone else's success and what you think they are good at, that may well be true, but they are

probably not good at what you are good at. Try to focus on your successes and not theirs.

8. Make a Happy Corner somewhere in your home and in that corner, place all of your awards, certificates, happy photographs and favourite quotes that inspire you or calm you. You could even write out words on a sheet of paper that describe your achievements or things that make you feel happy. It could be something really small to begin with. Here are a few examples:

- I scored a goal at our local community football match today, only one person scored that goal and it was me.
- I put my hand up in class or the meeting because I knew the answer, it made me feel good.
- My boss praised me today for all of the hard work that I do, it felt so nice to be appreciated.

Your Happy Corner will remind you that you are special and that you deserve to feel happy and calm and confident.

Have fun making your Happy Corner!

9. Affirmations are great! Use post-it stickers or pieces of paper or card. Stick them wherever you can see them regularly: in the kitchen, in your bedroom or, your bathroom. Write statements on them, for example:

- I am confident
- I deserve success
- I deserve happiness
- I deserve that promotion

There is a whole chapter in this book dedicated to affirmations, write out the ones that resonate with you and look at them several times a day. Put your favourite affirmation in your wallet or purse and carry it around with you.

10. Stress can make you overeat and so this is a daily affirmation that can be used, whenever you feel that compulsion to eat in-between meals. The affirmation can also be written on pieces of paper and stuck on the fridge or the cupboard doors in your kitchen. The affirmation could be worded 'I deserve to be slimmer'

11. Take five minutes out of your day every day and think about how good your life would be if you were slimmer.

12. Take a look in your wardrobe for an item of clothing that is in the size that you would love to be. Hang that item of clothing on the front of your wardrobe or the back of your bedroom door or where you can see it every day. That will be that outfits' 'home' until it fits you. If you are slimming down several sizes, then chunk this into realistic portions. The outfit that you hang up will be one size smaller and then when that fits you, replace it with an outfit the next size smaller. Keep your goals close and achievable.

13. Losing weight doesn't have to be all about restricting or denying yourself with the types of food that you eat and only eating diet food. Instead, learn to eat slightly differently. Eat the foods that you like but eat them slowly and consciously, which means focussing on what you are doing. It could be that you

sit and eat in front of the television and are so engrossed in what you are watching that before you know it, all the food on your plate has gone. You have eaten unconsciously. So the next time you eat, switch off the television whilst you are eating. If you have a table, sit down and eat your food there. Slow down to a quarter of the speed that you would normally eat at and count your chews. Try to go for twenty chews per mouthful and put your cutlery down in-between each mouthful. Most people do not put their cutlery down, instead, they busy themselves in getting the next mouthful ready on the end of the fork to shove it in. if you don't know what to do with your hands and I found this hard to begin with, just put your hands down at your side or hold them in your lap. When eating soft foods, for example, yoghurt or soup, count to twenty before you pick up the spoon and put the next mouthful in.

14. Eat from a smaller plate. I would suggest a side plate rather than a dinner plate. We have become so conditioned to eating large portions because of the freedom that we have to eat at restaurants or order food to take away that the portions are normally huge. Were you as a child brought up to finish the food on your plate? I was and so many other people were too. I was told to clear my plate. It was programming that your parents did unintentionally but it taught you to eat with your eyes. Eat all of the food on that plate and bypass the full signals from your stomach so that you become desensitised to them. I was guilt-tripped, even punished as I was born in that era. At times, the leftover dinner was served up to me for breakfast! Understandably, this

became a very deeply ingrained pattern and a way of eating. I know many adults that share this 'programming' with me.

If you can think back to your grandparents, their dinner plates were small but they seemed satisfied with the food on their plate. I never saw my grandparents having seconds or thirds.

Using a smaller plate 'tricks' your eyes into being satisfied with the amount of food on that plate. Your eyes will register 'a plate full of food'. Your eyes will help you to feel comfortable and happy with the portion size and as a result, you will eat less.

15. Take five minutes out each day and think about how you would like your life to be if all of the obstacles, all of the dramas were removed. Just daydream your perfect life. Daydreaming offers up very little resistance, rather than thinking 'I want this' or 'I need that' and your mind (Beryl) arguing with you that you don't deserve it, by daydreaming you are just 'picturing' something. This is a very clever trick because Beryl doesn't kick off if you are just 'daydreaming', not 'wanting' or 'needing'. The great thing and the real trick is that the human mind finds it virtually impossible to tell the difference between reality and something that has been vividly imagined. So, daydream away and remember dreams can come true!

I shall just finish this chapter with a true story.

Many years ago, I knew this guy. He was a nice man, very personable and good looking to boot! I could never understand why he didn't have a girlfriend. Over time, we became good friends and I broached the subject with him as to why he was single. He told me that he daydreamed every day about his perfect partner: a Hispanic who was beautiful inside and out.

One cold winter night with the rain lashing down outside, sitting in the warmth of his lounge and listening to some music, he heard a knock on his door. He ignored it at first but the knocking was persistent, eventually, he got up and opened the door. There standing in front of him on his doorstep was a woman; she was soaked through to the skin. She explained that her car had broken down and that her phone had run out of battery. She had felt that she had no choice but to knock on doors until someone answered.

My friend invited her in (he is very kind) and offered her a towel, a warm cup of tea and let her use his phone. Whilst they waited for help to arrive, they talked and by the time her help arrived, they had arranged a date.

To cut a long story short, she was the woman of my friend's daydreams: Hispanic and beautiful on the inside and out. They are now happily married and have a son.

So.........daydream away and remember dreams can come true!

CHAPTER SIX

AFFIRMATIONS

The glories of your existence are yet to be realised. In your darkest moments, your eyes will close to that which would lift you out of the depths. Seek your courage in joys and beauties that surround you, no matter what state of distress or pain is present in your being. The goodness of life does not disappear and is constant. Lift your eyes and see and your burdens will be lightened and your heart will sing again.

Little Owl Cards 2

Affirmations are a great idea because the mind responds to repetition, which in turn creates new neural pathways in the brain which then create new habits. So that your mind doesn't offer up resistance to your chosen affirmation, daydream as you say your affirmation, for example, 'what I think I become.'

If you are in a negative mindset, your mind could have a field day with this one. What if you just sat for a couple of minutes and daydreamed about how it would feel if you could be the person that you would love to be?

I would like to be…? I would love to be…? I would love to have…? Imagine that affirmation as real. See yourself living the life that the affirmation is stating. If it is safe, it is always a good idea to close your eyes as you daydream as this will make the process more powerful. Remember that the human mind finds it incredibly difficult to tell the difference between something that is real and something that is vividly imagined. The more that you can let go and daydream your affirmation, the more that daydream will become your reality.

Another example is 'today is a good day'. It doesn't matter how your day has started, if you got out of bed and stubbed your toe that could set you up for a bad day as your mindset instantly switches to negative with the pain of the stubbed toe. You may start thinking to yourself, 'that's a bad start to the day, that's an omen as to how my day is going to be'. As you are in a negative mindset, like a boomerang, like a magnet, negative things will be drawn into your life to affirm your 'negative affirmation' and so to counteract the 'negative affirmation' that began with the stubbed toe, flip the coin and say to yourself, 'even though I stubbed my toe this morning, today is a good day'.

You could carry your favourite affirmations around with you, perhaps write one or two on a small piece of card and keep them in your purse or your wallet. You can write them on sticky notes and stick them in places where you will see them regularly: your bathroom mirror, your kitchen cupboard, the dashboard in your car.

Here is a whole list that you can use, remember just choose the ones that resonate with you. As your energy begins to change to a more positive energy, your affirmations will begin to change too so then would be the time to choose some new affirmations to work with.

Have a look through them all and pick out any that you like. These will become your affirmations that you can use as many times during the day as you think of them.

- Today is a brand new day with different possibilities.
- What I think I shall become.
- I shall smile at a stranger today.
- I shall be kind today and help someone.
- I shall look for things today that I can be thankful for.
- I am beautiful.
- Today will be a good day.
- Life is for living.
- I can be strong.
- Worrying is just a way of thinking about things.
- I choose joy today.
- I deserve a good life.
- I trust my intuition. If it feels good, it is. If it feels bad, it is.
- I now release and let go of everything that no longer serves me.
- I will never give up on my dreams.
- I will walk away from anything that gives me bad vibes.
- I now choose to stick around positive people.
- I let go of what I can't control and surrender it.

- I dare to have the courage to be comfortable with being me. If others wish to judge or criticise then it is their problem and not mine.
- Yesterday has gone, tomorrow hasn't happened yet, I focus on what is happening now and I allow it to be a good now.
- I shall keep going and let the positive changes begin.
- Every time I catch a negative thought I shall flip it to a positive one, even if at first I have to pretend and the more that I do this, the more positive thoughts will become my reality.
- It's ok to allow myself to be happy.
- Time to let go of the crap.
- It's ok to forgive myself.
- I deserve to live my happiest life; I no longer doubt the power within me.
- I focus on what I wish to attract in my life, not what I want to let go of.
- My thoughts are not facts.
- I have all the answers within me.
- I am calm and in control.
- No matter what others think, I can believe in myself.
- I am positive.
- I am confident.
- I allow myself to fulfil my dreams.
- Today is a good day.
- This year is my year.
- Life is about choice, what I choose today will change my life for the better.

- I choose success as my only option.
- Change can happen in an instant.
- Will I commit to the fears or the good stuff today?
- I am learning to get out of my way and listen to my gut.
- All of my dreams are possible.
- I love myself.
- I believe in me.
- I am letting go of any self-limiting beliefs that no longer serve me.
- What can I change in my world today?
- I embrace my imperfect perfect self.
- If I believe in myself, everything is possible.
- Whatever happened yesterday, I choose to let go because today is the start of the rest of my life.
- Dream big, everything is possible.
- Change is scary, take a deep breath, be brave and just do it.
- Human beings are not perfect so I give myself a break and cut myself some slack.
- I no longer compare myself to others.
- I love and accept myself for who I am.
- I love myself and I am worthy of love.
- I can accomplish whatever I set my mind to accomplish.
- My life matters.
- I am worthy of a good life.
- It's a good day to be happy.
- I can be my true self.

- The more I let go of the negative stuff, the better I will feel.
- If I'm not controlling my thoughts then who is.
- What's normal anyway? I'm proud of the real me.
- I refuse to be disrespected by others.
- I refuse to disrespect myself.
- The right people will love me for just being me.
- I walk away from people that put me down.
- I cannot change others but I can change myself and that change changes everything.
- I forgive myself.
- Showing emotions is a sign of strength; it's ok to be sensitive.
- I do things because I want to do them, not because I want to please others.
- I am stepping back into my own personal power.
- I may not believe this yet but I am amazing.
- I believe in the magic of the law of attraction.
- I shall be the best that I can be today.
- I am a human magnet, what I think and feel will be drawn to me and so, I choose positive thoughts and feelings.
- I live each day as though it is a second chance at life.
- I am in control.
- I am no longer a prisoner of my past; it was just a lesson, not a life sentence.
- I am going to be so positive today that negative people cannot penetrate my shiny happy bubble.
- It's ok to say no and still be a nice person.

- When it rains, look for rainbows.
- When I put my hand over my heart and feel it beating, I am reminded that I am alive for a purpose.
- Everyone makes mistakes in life, it's called being human.
- It is time to reclaim my power.
- I am way more than enough.
- I shall laugh more today.
- I am worthy of love, peace and happiness.
- I am going to focus on what makes me happy.
- I am not selfish, I am selfless and there is a big difference.
- I am unique and I am beautiful.
- I believe anything is possible.

I hope that the list of affirmations will help you today, tomorrow, next week, next month and next year. Continue to use them, choosing just one or two to work with at a time. As you begin to feel that you're in a better place, replace the affirmations with new ones.

CHAPTER SEVEN

MEDITATIONS FOR ANXIETY, STRESS AND COPING WITH BULLYING

Dear dear soul. How we wish to touch your eyelids and transform them into light. How we wish to touch your lips and bring words of joy and happiness to your heart. How we wish to touch your heart and bring warmth and peace so that you may rest serene. When you put your trust in us we will do all these things. You only have to call and we will come to your side in an instant and you will no longer feel alone.

Little Owl Cards 2

You can either read the following meditations or use a recording device like your phone and play your voice back to yourself. If you dislike the sound of your voice, ask someone else to record the meditations for you.

Alternatively, you can email me at www.tamsincooper.co.uk and I will send you a copy of the audio. Each of these audios retails at £10 each but as a reader of this book, if you use code 711 in your email, I will send you the audio absolutely FREE.

When you listen to these meditation audios, please ensure that you are not driving or operating machinery.

Chinese Lanterns

TO BE USED FOR STRESS AND ANXIETY

Allow yourself to become as comfortable as you would wish to be. As you sit in that chair or lay in your bed, snuggle yourself down and when you're ready, allow your eyes to gently close.

I'd like you to begin to think about your breathing… thinking about breathing is something that most people ever rarely do, it is something that our bodies do automatically. Most people tend to breathe too shallow, so I would like you to try finding a level of breathing that feels exactly right for you: not too fast and not too slow.

Try to breathe all the way down into your stomach… take your time because you have all the time in the world, this is your time and your time alone. No one around to bother you or to trouble you, just your time…

I'd like you to be aware of any sounds that you can hear: inside or outside your room and allow those sounds to gently soothe you, reminding you that you are safe.

In a moment, I am going to help you to relax. If there is an emergency that you need to deal with you will simply open your eyes, deal with it and then return to this place of comfort.

Now, I'd like you to begin to breathe a bit deeper, just a little bit deeper now. Place your hands on your stomach and just feel how your hands gently rise and fall with every breath that you take...

Your mind will be filled with many thoughts, so many different thoughts. There's no need to try to fight with them or try to push them to one side. Just let them in. Let your mind think about whatever it wishes to think about. Allow the thoughts to just float in and then float back out again, like clouds. Focus on your breathing, deeper and deeper. Enjoy how it feels to sit or lay so still, with your eyes closed.

Be aware of just how comfortable your feet feel and focus on your back, just resting. As you begin to allow yourself to relax, you may experience the sensation of your back sinking down into the softness of your chair or bed.

I want you to use your imagination to develop a sense or a feeling that you have x-ray eyes. Imagine scanning your body all the way down from your head, all the way down to your feet, seeking out any tension or tightness that you may be holding in your muscles. Imagine scanning for that tension, all the way down, through your muscles: loosening, relaxing and letting go. All that tension simply melting away. Feel your muscles softening, becoming limp and relaxed. You may even begin to feel your body becoming heavier now.

This is your time, your time alone- no one to bother you, no one to trouble you, no one to demand anything from you- just relaxing down, all the way down, from the top of your head, all the way down to the very tips of your toes.

Feel your eyes becoming heavier now, all of those tiny muscles around your eyes just loosening and letting go- beginning to feel peaceful, feeling calm, feeling content, feeling safe.

Once more using your imagination, I'd like you to imagine that it's a warm summer evening and you are sitting on the sun terrace of a lovely hotel that overlooks the sea. Imagine that you are sitting in a chair that is soft and comfortable. You can feel the last rays of the sun warming you, a gentle breeze caressing your skin. You look out to the ocean, out to the sea and watch the sun beginning to go down. Beautiful colours fill the sky: purples, mauves, reds, oranges, yellows and gold, reflected on the water surface captured like glistening jewels in the tiny crests of the small waves. Maybe you can hear the sound of the gulls, the sound of the ocean, waves lapping onto the shore below you. Perhaps you can smell the clean salty air, a pleasant smell.

There is no one around, it's just you and you feel safe, so peaceful and so calm, just sitting there watching the sun going down, beginning to sink on the horizon disappearing into the sea. The air is still warm and you feel content just to sit and watch as the first stars begin to appear, twinkling in the night sky as the sky becomes as dark and as beautiful as midnight velvet. A full moon is reflected on the surface of the ocean.

Before you on the table are six Chinese lanterns, a box of matches, some sheets of paper and a pen. As you sit there, you begin to think about some of the things in your life that you would like to let go of. Things that give you negative thoughts and feelings- make you feel anxious, stressed, worried frustrated- make you lack confidence and hold you back- prevent you from moving forward with your life. Some of those things, you may feel that you have no control over but for this moment in time, as you sit there on that sun terrace so comfortably, feeling peaceful and safe, you feel brave enough to let them go.

Imagine your life and how good it would be if you could feel confident and relaxed all the time. Imagine yourself for a moment in a situation that would normally make you feel stressed, worried, anxious, unsure of yourself...

Now I want you to imagine yourself in that situation but looking happy, relaxed, confident: maybe it's your body language, a certain look in your eyes, you smiling perhaps. Just imagine yourself looking and feeling relaxed and confident. You know that life is very good to you and seeing yourself so peaceful, content, calm and confident, how wonderful that must feel!

As you picture yourself sitting in that safe place, in that comfortable chair, watching the sea, the ocean, the twinkling of so many diamond-bright stars in the night sky and listening to the sounds that you can hear, you begin to realise that there are different parts of you.

...there is the part that knows all about you, that keeps you alive and healthy but there is another part of you: a part of you that you have allowed unintentionally to fill you with unresourceful thoughts and unresourceful feelings. It's almost as if you have been in a relationship with a bully. Imagine if someone you loved, your partner, family member or, a friend was being bullied, how would you advise them to deal with that bully? Would you stand up to that bully on their behalf? So why put up with that bully inside you? It is finally time to let go of that bully.

On the table before you, I want you to start writing on the sheets of paper. I want you to write on each sheet of paper one word that describes the things you are willing to let go of. Just one word on each sheet of paper.

When you have done this, attach each sheet to one of the Chinese lanterns and when you are ready to let go of these things, light the lanterns one by one and watch them float up into the night sky. How beautiful the lanterns look! You are mesmerised as you watch the lanterns being caught by the gentlest of breezes, becoming higher and higher taking with them those things that for now, you can let go of.

You can begin to feel lighter within yourself as if some heavy weight has been lifted from you. As you watch the lanterns become smaller and smaller in the vast expanse of the night sky, drifting out across the ocean, you see that they have become tiny little lights now. You begin to feel that all is well in your world. A warm, easy and comfortable feeling beginning to grow from somewhere deep inside of you, as you watch those lanterns becoming so small that they disappear. Leaving you feeling lighter, calmer and really good about yourself.

These quiet, calm, confident and peaceful feelings will now stay with you for as long as you need them. Calm, peaceful feelings that will now build within you a quiet strength and a determination to achieve your hopes and dreams. A determination to succeed, whatever success means to you, will become stronger and stronger as each day passes.

BULLYING

Bullying can cause stress and anxiety.

This is a meditation to help you to cope with bullying at school, home or, in the workplace.

Take as long as you need to get yourself nice and comfortable in a place where you feel safe. When you are ready, let your eyes close.

As you sit there or lay there, your mind may be thinking of lots of different things: some good thoughts and some thoughts that may be making you feel uncomfortable and unhappy.

Snuggle down as I help you to let go of those unhappy feelings and thoughts so that you can become stronger, happier, more self-assured and confident.

Allow your mind to drift, thinking about whatever it wishes to think about. There is no need to fight with those thoughts or try to quieten them down. Just let those thoughts in because as they drift in, they will soon drift back out again.

Now let your body begin to relax enough for you to feel comfortable so that you can take on board the suggestions that I say to help you to become happier, stronger and no longer a victim to bullying.

Beginning with your feet, I want you to imagine scrunching your feet up, really tighten those small muscles, try to curl your feet up into balls and then let them relax. Do the same with your calf muscles, scrunch them tight, hold them for a few seconds and then let them relax. Move on up to your thigh muscles and do the same, scrunch, hold and, then let go. You may begin to feel your legs becoming heavier. Try and tighten your stomach muscles, tighten them as much as you can, hold and then let go. Chest muscles next, try to tighten them, hold and then let them relax. Your arm muscles, squeeze them, hold and then let go, relax. Hunch your shoulders and squeeze your shoulder blades together as hard as you can, hold, let go and relax them. Imagine any tension in your neck just simply melting away. Open your mouth slightly and rest your tongue on the bottom of your mouth behind your bottom teeth and let your tongue rest just there. Imagine that you can feel the tiny muscles around your eyes loosening and relaxing.

Bullies are normally attracted to people because of something that cannot be seen. It's like a sixth sense: it could be because you feel unhappy **or** sad about something **or** you feel shy, **or** not very confident **or** you are scared of something **or** you are desperate to fit in. It makes the bully feel strong. However, I am going to let you into a big secret – bullies are cowards – they pick on people that they feel stronger over and the reason that they do this is to make themselves feel strong because actually, they aren't strong. They are weak, scared, frightened and insecure and you are stronger than they are. It's all a big act on their part.

So, let's flip the coin, you are going to become confident and you are going to learn to feel really good about yourself.

You are going to learn how to become incredibly strong inside.

And to do this, I want you to imagine that you are someone that you see as popular or happy or strong. I want you to imagine as you sit there or lay there that you could float up out of yourself and float down into that person. It may be someone that you know in real life, it could be someone that you have seen in a movie or read about in a book.

Nobody will know what you are doing because you are imagining this within yourself.

Imagine what it would feel like to be that person? What does it feel like? I am sure that it must feel wonderful. I want you to imagine spending a few moments imagining that you are inside that person. Be that person, breathe the way you think that person breathes, imagine thinking the way that person thinks. Do you think they would stand any nonsense from that bully? How do they sit? How do they stand? How do they deal with the problems in their life? Just take a few minutes to daydream as you imagine being a part of that person.

THE GOOD NEWS IS THAT YOU CAN BECOME JUST LIKE THAT PERSON.

You see, our minds find it hard to tell the difference between something that is real and something that is vividly imagined so every time you pretend or imagine being that person, a little bit of them will become a part of you. Isn't that good news?

Repeat these words to yourself in your mind:

- I am likeable.
- I feel comfortable being me.
- I am strong.
- I am worthy.
- I am special.
- I deserve to feel good.
- I am loved.
- I feel sorry for that cowardly bully.
- I can stand up to that bully.
- The bully no longer holds any power over me.
- I am powerful.
- My nerves will grow stronger and stronger every day.
- I feel calm.
- I am peaceful.
- I have a sense of wellbeing.
- I feel good.
- My life is good.

CHAPTER EIGHT

POSITIVE THINKING AND SLEEP

MEDITATIONS

If you feel terrific notify your face.

Little Owl Cards 2

Here are two more meditations that you can either read or use a recording device to record for yourself.

Alternatively, you can email me at www.tamsincooper.co.uk and I will send you a copy of the audio. Remember to mention the code 711 so that you can receive the meditation absolutely FREE.

Do not drive or operate machinery whilst listening to the two meditations in this chapter.

Positive Thinking

To be used to help you to think positively and to reduce stress and anxiety

It is time to clear all of the negativity out of your life so that you can have a more positive life for yourself. No matter how hard you tried before, it just didn't seem to happen. All the good times were short-lived and you just seem to be stuck in this negative frame of mind that you haven't been able to break away from. Now it is time for you to have a happier life. When you think positively, the magic begins and life starts changing.

So let's begin.

Get yourself nice and comfortable. It doesn't matter if you are sitting in a chair or lying in your bed. As you sit or lay there, you will be aware of the sounds that you can hear and the sounds will remind you that you are safe.

Now gently allow your eyes to close. Just close your eyes. Be aware of your body and start working your way down to find any tension that you may be holding in any of your muscles, starting from your forehead. Imagine those muscles smoothing out.

Now work your way down through your face to your jaw, is your jaw clenched? You can loosen it by opening your mouth slightly and resting your tongue on the bottom of your mouth, let the bottom of your jaw just hang down.

Those muscles in your neck and shoulders are where we tend to hold our stresses, they may feel tight. Imagine those muscles uncoiling. All that tension just simply melting away, literally feel your shoulders sinking down. Focus on the muscles in your chest and stomach, they may feel clenched and tight. You may experience a knotted feeling in your stomach. Now imagine those muscles softening and being replaced with a comfortable feeling, a feeling of wellbeing.

The muscles in your back are softening too, perhaps you are experiencing the sensation of your back slowly sinking down, down into the softness of your chair or bed. You are really relaxing now. Focus on your arms and imagine all those muscles relaxing: your upper arms down to your elbows, forearms, down to your wrists, your hands, your fingers. Imagine any tension in your arms just flowing away through your fingertips, allowing your arms to rest so comfortably. Focus on your legs, all those muscles from your thighs all the way down, down to the tips of your toes. All those muscles softening as any tension in your legs is flowing out through the tips of your toes, resting so comfortably now.

Your mind may have so many different thoughts. Some of those thoughts may be about how you would like your life to be while some thoughts will be about other things. Allow your mind to think about whatever it wants to and allow it to wander off wherever it wishes to go, it's ok, it really doesn't matter.

I'm going to ask you to use your imagination now and I would like you to imagine a hot summer day and you find yourself standing at the bottom of a mountain. There is a part of you that is feeling compelled to climb this mountain. You don't know the reason why, all that you know is that you just have to do it.

You find yourself wearing a pair of sturdy climbing shoes and before you, stands a man and he hands you a rucksack and tells you that it contains some tools to help you with the climb. You pick up the rucksack and swing it onto your back, thanking the man and you begin to climb the mountain.

At first, there is a kind of makeshift pathway and you think to yourself that this is easier than you thought it would be. You make slow but steady progress admiring all of the tiny wild flowers you see along the way. However, as you climb, the path begins to disappear and you have to use your instinct to navigate your ascent. Every so often, you stop to take a break and you notice that the air is becoming thinner and you now have the challenge of not only focusing on your climb but also your breathing. You begin to notice that the rucksack on your back is now becoming heavier and heavier and so many times, you try to take it off. You decide that you can make do without the tools inside it but every time you try to remove the rucksack, you discover that it feels well and truly stuck to you. You cannot take it off. After several attempts, you resign yourself to the fact that as you climb this mountain, the rucksack is coming with you, no matter what.

The higher the climb, the steeper it becomes. The harder it is, the heavier the rucksack. As you stop to try to catch your breath, you think to yourself about how your life is like an uphill struggle. You feel like giving up as this task that you have set yourself is beginning to feel overwhelming and yet there is something inside you that is urging you on. As you climb now, you focus on how heavy the rucksack has become and again you try to release it but it is stuck firmly to your back.

You don't understand how this is happening and you begin to feel resentful, saying to yourself 'why is this happening to me? what have I done to deserve this? why am I climbing this mountain? I didn't want to do this in the first place!' You feel that you want to cry with the frustration and the injustice of it all. Three-quarters of the way up the mountain, you see a bottle of water. With a spurt of energy, you make your way over to it. Not only is it a welcome sight but it is also ice-cold, refreshingly ice-cold. You don't understand how on earth a bottle of water, a bottle of cold water could appear out of nowhere but you quickly push that thought out of your mind as you unscrew the top and down the contents in one. You can feel the coldness as you swallow the water, feeling it flowing down your throat and into your stomach, totally refreshing you. Just what you needed.

With a renewed determination you look up, still very aware of the rucksack. This heavy weight on your back and shoulders is still there but at last, the top of the mountain is in sight. Now you begin to count the steps to help yourself focus on reaching the summit. One, two, three, four, up you go, five, six, you're almost there.. seven, keep going, eight, nine, ten. You are at the top. Your legs feel all wobbly, like jelly and you spot a bench in front of you. You somehow manage to walk over to the bench and flop yourself down and take a deep breath. You've made it. For a moment you close your eyes and just take a few deep breaths, just a few deep breaths...

You are aware of that rucksack digging in your shoulders and you wriggle yourself trying to free it. Incredibly, you find that you can at last take the rucksack off. Using both arms because of the weight, you place it on the ground, still feeling resentful towards it. If you could have managed the journey up the mountain without it, things would have been a lot easier, you think to yourself.

Curiosity makes you open the bag and you discover it is packed full of rocks. This comes as a complete surprise to you as the man had told you that the contents held tools to help you climb. 'What kind of cruel trick was this', something at the back of your mind whispers, 'are you really surprised?' Life has rarely been fair to you.

You begin to take the rocks out one by one. Some are large and some are quite small. You then realise as you place them before you that each one is covered in writing. You pick the nearest one up to you and inspect what is written on it and what you read almost takes your breath away. The words accurately describe the challenges in your life. You pick up another rock and there written on its surface is another of your challenges, problems and worries. You pick up a third.

I want you now to look at all the rocks. Each rock describes a negative aspect in your life that if you could, you would love to get rid of it. Take some moments to yourself as you look at all the worries, frustrations, stresses written on those rocks…

Pick them all up one by one and look at them…

You now have a choice. You can either keep the rocks or throw them away. You have a choice. What do you want to do? Do you want to keep them or do you want to throw them away? Is there any part of you that feels the need to keep these rocks? Sometimes, change can make you feel scared even when it is a good change because change always means to a certain extent, stepping into the unknown. So if any part of you is worried about throwing away those rocks, I want you to imagine just for a moment how good your life could be if you could only focus on positives. How different your life would be if all of the negative barriers were removed. Take a few moments to yourself as you think about how good your life could be…

You have made up your mind. You want to have a good life, you deserve a good life. Gather up the rocks and move towards the side of the mountain. You can sit or stand, it is your choice. You look down and as far as you can see, there is a beautiful flat landscape: fields, trees and roads. The scenery beneath you is beautiful. Begin to roll those rocks down the side of the mountain one by one. You watch as they pick up speed, landing on the ground below. Throw away every single one of them. As you roll each one down, notice a good feeling growing inside you. A great feeling. A feeling of wellbeing. When all the rocks have gone, you lay back on the grass and feel the warmth of the sun on your skin and close your eyes, feeling a sense of peace and tranquillity, knowing that all will be well.

And as each new day dawns, this feeling of inner peace will now begin to create a feeling of inner strength inside you. It'll help you to achieve your hopes and desires, your dreams and your goals. I wish you success!

SLEEP WELL

Stress and anxiety can disrupt your sleep patterns.

This meditation will help you to regain the habit to sleep well.

As you lay in your bed, settle yourself down and get yourself nice and comfortable. With your eyes open, begin to notice the rhythm of your breathing. Notice the way your chest rises and falls. Take a really deep breath and slowly breathe out. And again, breathing in deeply and slowly breathing out. Allow your breathing to return to its normal rhythm for a couple of moments. Now begin to find a slower comfortable rhythm of breathing. Take your time, notice the difference, you can feel your breathing becoming even slower and steadier. Begin to breathe more deeply now. Feel your body beginning to relax as you focus on your breathing.

You begin to start to feel a sense of comfort. Every time you feel your eyes blinking, you will experience the sensation of your eyelids becoming heavier and heavier. Beginning now to develop a sense of inner comfort, feel the tension and worries beginning to melt away. You are becoming sensitive to the feelings of your body. You can notice where any covers or clothes touch your skin, where your hair perhaps brushes against your face. How your head feels as it lays on your pillow and you feel your head sinking into your pillow.

Take a deep breath in and out and allow your eyes to gently close and feel the comfort of your closed eyes. Every time you breathe out, feel yourself sinking down into a relaxed calmness. Every time you breathe out, associate that breath with your body relaxing more and more. As you do this, you become sensitive to the tension in your muscles. Breathe in slowly and then as you slowly breathe out, imagine breathing out those tensions. Imagine breathing those tensions away from you.

Focus your mind on your toes and feet and ankles. Breathe in slowly and as you breathe slowly out, relax those muscles and imagine releasing the tension from your toes and feet and ankles.

Allow your mind to think about the muscles from your ankles to your thighs. Visualise this area of your body from your ankles to your thighs. This time as you breathe in, get ready so that when you breathe out, you can allow every muscle, every fibre, every nerve to relax all the way down, down through those muscles and continue down to the tips of your toes.

Slowly breathing in and slowly breathing out and feel yourself relaxing more and more. Breathe in and slowly breathe out. Feel yourself relaxing more and more.

Visualise your body from your thighs up to your chest and include the muscles in your back. Visualise that whole area from your thighs all the way up to your chest. Slowly breathe in and slowly breathe out, breathing down all the way down to the tips of your toes and again, slowly breathe in and imagine a wave of relaxation starting from your toes up through your body and chest. As you breathe out, feel that wave of relaxation travelling down through your body, down your back and spine, chest and stomach, releasing any tension, any stress, any anxiety. Down through your legs and down to your toes. Take a slow breath in and out. Really relaxing now.

Visualise that wave of relaxation spreading up through your toes, thighs, chest, back, shoulders and neck. Any tension in your shoulders and neck, just simply melting away like fluid as you breathe slowly out. Breathe that wave down into your muscles all the way to the tips of your toes, leaving your muscles feeling soft. Breathe in and visualise all the muscles in your face and as you breathe out, feel the muscles in your jaw relaxing and the muscles in your face relaxing too- your eyes, your forehead.

Slowly breathe in and visualise a wave of relaxation slowly coming up from the tips of your toes to the top of your head and slowly breathe out. Your body relaxing more and more, feel your body sinking down and down into the softness of your bed. Drifting down into comfort, really relaxing now, sinking down into calmness. Breathe again, breathing in slowly and breathe out. Beginning to feel so comfortable and so peaceful now. Going deeper and deeper, feel how relaxed, how relaxed your whole body is becoming.

As your body relaxes, your mind can relax too. All the tension, worries and stresses, all melting away now. Surrender to this lazy, calm, drifting, peaceful, relaxing feeling. This comfortable feeling is so restful that you may even fall asleep.

In a moment, you will open your eyes and count from one to three and stare ahead. Then you will close your eyes. Your eyelids will feel even heavier and you will feel yourself drifting further and further into an easy and peaceful sleep.

Open your eyes, stare ahead now.. one, two, three.. close your eyes. Your eyes are becoming heavier now and your body is feeling even more relaxed.

Allow yourself to drift, you may have a feeling of drifting down and down. You are drifting deeper and deeper into a natural sleep. Feel the stillness of your body and mind. Let a sense of that stillness start to grow. Perhaps your mind could picture the stillness of a beautiful lake, a softly rising mist on the still surface of the lake. You know that within yourself, deep inside yourself, there is a stillness. Feel that stillness inside you. Feel how still you can be. Gentle responses are going on in your body, as your body now prepares to sleep. Feel how warm and comfortable your body feels, so very comfortable, so very peaceful now. Feel how loose and limp your jaw is becoming.

I want you to imagine now a soft light filtering down. Imagine seeing yourself surrounded by soft light. Imagine feeling that light all around, comforting you, soothing you. Each time now you breathe in, you breathe in relaxation and each time you breathe out, you are relaxing deeper and deeper.

Imagine you could feel the light flowing to every part of your body, soothing and calming, relaxing your body. Preparing you to sleep. Each time you breathe out, you are becoming more and more comfortable, more and more peaceful. As you lay there in your bed, I want you to think about all the lovely things in your life. Spend a few moments thinking about all of the wonderful things in your life. Things in your life that you can be thankful for. As you think about all of the lovely positive things in your life, I'm going to help you to relax even more so that you can naturally and easily drift into a restful sleep. I'm going to count down from five down to one and on each number down, you will find yourself sleepier and sleepier.

Five, beginning to drift down.

Four, feel yourself becoming sleepier and sleepier.

Three, feel a gentle and welcoming heaviness spreading now through the whole of your body.

Two, drifting down now.

One, feeling so calm, so peaceful, relaxed, drifting naturally and easily into sleep.

As you lay there, you allow your body to welcome this sleepy state. Allowing your mind to feel settled and calm, just laying in this peaceful, restful and, drowsy state. Feeling really calm, peaceful. Feeling drowsy and sleepy.

You will find sleep coming easily to you and you will begin to look forward to bedtime.

Your body feeling safe as you drift naturally, easily and effortlessly into a beautiful and restful sleep. Drifting now into a natural, beautiful and restful sleep. Your body relaxing more and more as you drift into sleep.

CHAPTER NINE

WEIGHT LOSS AND PAIN

MANAGEMENT MEDITATIONS

Are you flying in the face of your destiny? Are you doing what your inner senses are prodding you to do? Think harder. Stop and take stock. Look ahead to possible consequences. Then you will be able to go ahead or change direction according to your true feelings. Your inner feelings know what is right for you, personally.

Little Owl Cards 2

Here are two more meditations for you to either read or record for yourself. Remember, if you would like an audio copy please email me tamsin@tamsincooper.co.uk using the code 711 so that you can receive and enjoy the recordings absolutely free.

The first meditation will help you to manage your weight easily, help you to control comfort eating, stress eating or, eating for every emotion, and, even when life is challenging.

The second meditation is for pain management. When you are in pain, it can make you feel more short-tempered and stressed, this meditation will help you to manage the pain and stay calmer.

Weight Loss

Make yourself comfortable in your favourite chair or your bed. Allow me to help you to relax because when the body relaxes, the mind can relax and when the mind relaxes changes can begin to happen.

Allow your eyes to close and listen to all the sounds that you can hear all around you. The sounds remind you that life is continuing as you take this time out, just for you, so that you can focus on making changes to help yourself become slimmer, happier and healthier.

You may start to feel sleepy or very relaxed and that's ok. If for any reason you need to open your eyes you will immediately be alert but for now, snuggle yourself down into your chair or bed.

Focus on your closed eyes and imagine the hundreds of tiny muscles around your eyes beginning to relax, your eyes may even begin to feel heavier now. Allow a feeling of relaxation to begin to flow down, all the way down through your body, like a gentle wave. As your body begins to relax, any stress or tension that you may be holding in any of your muscles will begin to simply melt away.

Feel the muscles in your jaw beginning to relax and your tongue rests gently on the bottom of your mouth behind your teeth. The muscles in the neck where we can hold tension now softening and relaxing. The muscles in your shoulders just letting go. Feel your chest and stomach muscles relaxing and your back muscles too, muscles all the way down your spine, softening, relaxing and, letting go.

Feel a soft wave moving down through your arms, enveloping your elbows, wrists, hands and fingertips. Focus on your legs, relaxing down to your knees, ankles, feet, and toes.

You are beginning to feel so comfortable.

I don't know the reasons why you want to lose weight. Maybe you want a slimmer, healthier, fitter body. Maybe you have been slim in the past but then began to eat differently and made poor choices. Or maybe you have always just wanted to be slimmer but bad habits always stopped you. All that matters now is: you want to make a change and that you want a slimmer and healthier body.

You can become slimmer without dieting. You can become slimmer just by eating normal food, foods that you like. You will begin to adopt healthier choices and eating habits and this will begin to occur easily and naturally.

You will now begin to focus on taking care of yourself, eating just three small meals a day and your focus will be seeing your body becoming slimmer. Hang a favourite item of clothing on the outside of your wardrobe one size smaller. This will be it's 'home' until it fits you. When it fits you, you will then replace it with another favourite item of clothing in the next size down. You will continue this until you become the size you wish to be.

You deserve to accept compliments and soon you will become comfortable accepting compliments. Feel proud of what you are achieving: you are taking responsibility, you are becoming healthier, and you are beginning to feel more comfortable in your skin. You are beginning to like 'you' again and you are regaining your confidence and your self-esteem. You place notes on your fridge and food cupboards 'I am in control of my eating habits'.

You create a simple exercise regime, one that you can fit in easily into your daily lifestyle. Be kind to yourself, not everyone likes going to the gym. 10 minutes of exercise a day is better than setting yourself an impossible goal. You can even exercise by parking your car in the furthest point at the supermarket.

Use the stairs at work rather than the lift.

If you have a dog, walk your dog a further 5 or 10 minutes a day.

Place the kid's lunch boxes by the front door rather than filling them up on the kitchen side and take the lunch items one by one, banana, sandwich, drink and before you know it, you will have walked an extra 400 steps.

Run up and down the stairs at home.

Put an exercise bike in your lounge, and sit and cycle rather than slouching on the sofa at night watching television.

When you walk, speed up your pace.

The list is endless, use your imagination.

Make an exercise chart and put it in your kitchen, somewhere you can see it every day. Create easily achievable ways that you can move your body that you can fit into your lifestyle. Try to aim for 30 minutes a day; you could also chunk the exercise into 3 lots of 10 minutes. Small ways that you can accommodate into your life that will make a difference.

When you eat, switch off your television, because when you eat in front of the television you are eating 'unconsciously' you are focusing on the television and not on what you are doing which is eating. Have you ever watched other people eat? They shovel the food in automatically and then before they know it all the food has gone. If you can when you eat, sit at a table and focus just on your eating. In between mouthfuls you now put your knife and fork down. You eat at a quarter of the speed and you chew every mouthful at least 20 times. If you are eating soft food still count to 20 before putting the next mouthful in. You now enjoy eating from a smaller plate, you will feel happier eating much smaller amounts. You begin to enjoy the taste of the food rather than the amount. You now listen and respond to the signal from your stomach that says you are comfortably full, you have had enough to eat and you find it easy to leave whatever food is left on your plate.

As you have allowed yourself to gain weight, you now allow your body to slim down, to shed away all that excess, simply and easily. Eat breakfast daily as this kick starts your metabolism. See your metabolism like a fire. When you feed that fire, it burns. During the night whilst you sleep, the fire gently smoulders, by eating breakfast the fire ignites and begins to burn again, your metabolism speeds up and you enjoy seeing how slim your body is becoming.

Drink water. Water now becomes your preferred choice of drink. You enjoy drinking a few glasses of delicious water in between your meals, this is becoming a normal habit for you.

I want you now to imagine seeing yourself in a mirror in one month, one size smaller. Now imagine seeing yourself in six months, so much slimmer. Now see yourself in a year with a body that you like. You love how you look and feel. You feel happy, you feel amazing. You deserve to be your new shape and size and it's ok to accept compliments. It feels so good to be able to wear the clothes you want to wear. To be able to go into a shop and pull something off the rack knowing that it will fit you. You have more energy and you can do all the things you've always wanted to do. You love being able to control your eating habits. Feeling empowered. Feeling fantastic.

Listen to the suggestions I make to help you to become the size you wish to be, the person you wish to be:

I deserve to be slim.

I deserve to have the body I feel comfortable in.

I have the power and the control to become whatever size I wish to be.

I feel happy eating just three small meals a day.

I prefer eating healthier options.

I love drinking delicious water.

I have more energy.

I look good.

I feel good.

I am in control.

This is the second meditation in this chapter:

Pain Management

As you sit there or lay there, I want you to take a moment to settle yourself into a comfortable position. Take your time, and when you are ready, let your eyes gently close. Take a deep breath and breathe in as deeply as you can and as you breathe out, breathe out as slowly as you can. Take 10 of these breaths, focusing on your breathing and as you do this, I want you to imagine that you could breathe in relaxation, and as you breathe out, imagine that you could breathe out any tension, stresses that you may be holding in your body. Focus now and count those 10 breaths, breathing nice and slow.

Allow the muscles in your body to begin to relax. The muscles in your forehead, give them permission to begin to relax and feel your brow becoming smoother and heavier. Just let those muscles relax. Just relaxing and letting go.

Now focus on the muscles in your cheeks, your mouth, and your jaw. Any tension that you may be holding in your face, imagine it just draining away like a fluid, draining down and away, leaving all those muscles relaxed and at ease.

Your neck muscles are now relaxing, just let those muscles relax. The more you can physically relax, the more you can mentally relax too. When you mentally relax, changes can begin to happen.

Now your shoulders, any tension there, just simply melting away as your shoulder muscles relax.

Now your arms, relaxing down to your elbows, your hands, your wrists, all the way down to your fingertips. You may notice that your arms feel heavier now.

Now your chest, allow your chest muscles to relax, and your stomach muscles too, your stomach muscles feeling really comfortable.

Notice your breathing and how it is becoming steadier and even. With every breath, you take, you are becoming more and more relaxed.

Feel a comforting, calming feeling beginning to grow inside your stomach. A feeling of peacefulness.

Your back muscles are softening, loosening, relaxing, and letting go. You may even experience the sensation of your back sinking down into the softness of your bed or your chair.

Thigh muscles now softening, feeling a wave of relaxation travelling down to your knees, your calves, down to your feet, and all the way down to your toes.

Feeling very calm, very peaceful now.

I want you to use your imagination, and imagine you are visiting a beautiful garden; this may be a garden that you know or just one that you would like to imagine. See before you a lush green lawn, you decide to take off your shoes, and you begin to walk barefoot across the grass, it feels soft and springy and cool beneath your feet.

In front of you are some steps, 10 old worn stone steps that lead down further into this beautiful garden. There is an air of peace and tranquillity here. The weather is perfect, just how you like it to be. You enjoy breathing in the clean, pure air.

In a moment, I'm going to say 'Now', and when I say now, you will begin to go down the steps. As you go down the steps, you will go deeper and deeper into relaxation. The steps are safe, they feel smooth and warm beneath your feet, and there is a railing to hold onto.

Now……..

10. Down you go, beginning to relax, beginning to let go.

9. Feeling more at ease, and at peace with yourself.

8. Perhaps noticing a restful feeling spreading all the way through your body.

7. Just drifting, deeper and deeper down now.

6. Becoming calmer and calmer.

5. Relaxing and letting go.

4. Sounds becoming a part of your experience and comfort.

3. Sinking deeper and deeper.

2. Enjoying these feelings, feeling safe.

1. Drifting deeper and deeper, down you go.

You step onto a small path that has been worn smooth by many that have walked this path before you. You can hear the sounds of water and as you walk, you stop every now and again to admire the wildflowers that grow in clusters by the edge of the path. It is safe to smell their perfume. You come to a stream, you sit down on the bank and watch as the water gently bubbles and gurgles, as it passes over small rocks and stones.

As you sit there, you begin to think about how your body is betraying you, letting you down and all you want is to be well and healthy. As you sit there lost in thought, an idea starts to form in your mind. It's almost like a lightbulb moment and you realise that how you are thinking about your illness is a dominant thought and what we think we become. So constantly thinking about how you feel, you have reinforced your illness. Now that you are aware of this, you are going to undo this negative pattern of thinking by thinking differently.

To achieve a healthier body, I want you, first of all, to locate the pain or the discomfort in your body. Now give that discomfort a shape, any shape will do. Perhaps a spiky shape or a shape with sharp edges, you decide. Using the power of your imagination, begin to shrink this shape down. Shrink it down quickly or slowly, it doesn't matter. All that matters is that you imagine shrinking that shape down. All the way down, until you have shrunk the shape down to the size of a pinhead. Give that pinhead a colour, a strong colour. You decide the colour, and when you have thought of the colour then imagine fading that colour out until the pinhead is transparent. Take your time until all that's left is a tiny small hole where the pinhead used to be.

Imagine once again sitting by the stream. The sun is beginning to set and the sky is filled with beautiful shades of pink, mauve and gold. You can still feel the warmth of the sun on your skin and you release a small sigh of contentment. Lay back in the soft grass feeling totally relaxed, warm, and at peace. As you lay there, you imagine that you are beginning to feel lighter and lighter, so light that you start to feel yourself floating up. You feel safe and you find yourself floating amongst the clouds. The clouds are coloured pink, mauve and gold. These are healing colours; your body begins to absorb them. You feel so very peaceful now. Just floating and allowing these healing colours to be absorbed into your body through the pores of your skin, through every breath. The gold, pink and mauve now seek out the tiny hole and they fill the hole with their healing and you watch as the hole seals up, making you whole again. You feel good, you feel well, you feel your energy returning as you float there, your body gently carried on the softest of warm breezes. Feel your body becoming healthy again.

A golden cloud surrounds your body and you feel yourself being lowered down, all the way down until you find yourself once again laying by the side of the stream. You are cocooned in soft golden light. It feels welcoming. The golden light scans down through your body from the top of your head, all the way down to the tips of your toes. It rejuvenates every part of you. As you lay there, you feel your energy levels increasing, any pain or discomfort being smoothed away and noticing spreading wellness now filling your entire body, every cell, organs, muscles, and every part of you being checked and repaired. You can feel your body filling with pure health. Stay in this golden light for as long as you wish to as your body returns to its strength. A sense of peace and calm and a feeling of wellness and wellbeing will now stay with you.

CHAPTER TEN

SOME MORE EXERCISES AND

CONCLUSION

When things start to pile up on you and you can't see how you can get them all done, step back and think. There is really no need to rush – there is time – the right time. Ease off, breathe again and begin on those things that demand your attention first and you will find that all others can wait. Your tension will disappear and what you do will be executed more joyfully.

Little Owl Cards 2

In this last chapter, I am going to begin by sharing another case study with you.

Case Study

I was first introduced to Jane when she was sixteen years old. Jane had not left the house for two years apart from going to the airport for a family holiday to Disney. Sadly, she suffered a panic attack at the airport at check-in and refused to continue the holiday adventure. The family was disappointed and torn as the holiday had cost an enormous amount of money but decided that they could not continue their holiday and they all returned home.

Jane had been home schooled for two years. Her routine, well, there was no routine except for the fact that she stayed awake all night and slept during the day. She was aware of the strain on her family but felt helpless to do anything about it. There was no apparent 'trigger' for her behaviour. Jane tried to cling onto some form of control but in vain. She had also developed OCD and a fear that close members of her family were going to die.

I worked with Jane and she began my stress management programme, also using some of the self-help exercises that are mentioned in this book. She began to progress well. On her seventeenth birthday, she not only had her last session with me but had also had her first driving lesson. She had also started seeing friends and socialising again and leaving the home.

That was three years ago. Now Jane has a job, a boyfriend, and drives. She also uses public transport which had been another fear. She no longer takes medication. Her life now is as it should be for a twenty-year-old; she feels calm, is confident and now experiences hope where there was only hopelessness before. SHE IS LIVING LIFE.

Before I finish this last chapter I would like to share with you five more exercises to help you deal with and overcome stress, worry, frustration, fear, anxiety, and control the negative chatterbox in your mind. The exercises will also help you to stay calm and supercharge up your immune system.

1. This exercise will help you to be mindful of those bad thoughts:

    Whenever you have a bad thought, try to be aware of it and acknowledge it because it is a part of you. Then simply dump it; put it on the naughty step. It takes a while to become aware of those thoughts so that you can 'catch' them but the more you practice, the better you will get at this exercise. You will learn to stop them in their tracks. Any negative thoughts that you have coming into you, get into the habit of noticing them, acknowledging them, importantly not accepting them, and then moving on so that you can free up your mind for more positive thoughts.

2. This exercise will help you to train your mind to work more positively:

    Work on your mindset every day. This could be meditation, or keeping a journal and writing a few things that you are grateful for. Maybe you write 3 or 4 things or maybe you write 10 things. It could be going for a walk, sending love to the universe, surrendering a problem to the universe if it feels too big for you to deal with, find your way. There is no right or wrong time to work on your mindset.

3. This exercise will help you to get rid of the stress, worries, fears, frustrations and stresses and anxieties:

    Get a pen and a piece of paper and I want you to write all of your worries and your frustrations down. Next, write all of your fears down and lastly all of your anxieties and your stresses. Take your time with this exercise, there's no need to hurry as it doesn't have to be rushed and completed in two minutes.

Whatever comes into your mind, whatever you are thinking, whatever you are feeling, write it all down. All of those negative thoughts and negative feelings.

Once you've written them down, if you can safely burn it, I want you to burn that piece of paper. If it isn't safe to burn it, tear the paper up into tiny pieces and then throw them in the bin. Those bits of paper are just rubbish. They are just worthless thoughts.

4. This is a powerful exercise that will help you to control the negative chatterbox in your mind, Beryl* from chapter two: the negative part of your mind that incessantly chatters away, criticising you, pulling you down, and making you feel bad about yourself.

The first thing I would like you to do is to locate the negative chatterbox in your head, it could be at the front or the back of your head, the top of your head or, to the side of your head.

You are now going to beat the negative chatterbox at its own game.

Now allow all of those negative thoughts to come into your mind, don't worry about this because we are going to deal with them. As they come into your mind, into that part of your head where you have located where your negative chatterbox is I want you to imagine turning those thoughts into a horrible, nasty brown, gloopy muddy liquid.

Allow that liquid to run down through your head, down your neck, across your shoulders, down into your arms and, into your hands. Imagine now that you are holding a ball in your hands. The ball can be any size, any colour (I always imagine my ball as a transparent plastic ball). Imagine that liquid transferring from your hands and going into the ball. Continue allowing all those negative thoughts to change into that liquid, running down through your head and arms and into your hands.

I like using the transparent ball because I can imagine seeing that liquid filling up my ball.

Eventually, your mind will run out of negative stuff to say, and this is when the fun part starts.

You are going to get rid of the ball! Use your imagination here! Imagine throwing your ball out of a plane, tossing it over the side of a boat out at sea, and watch it bobbing away from you on the ocean waves. Fasten a rocket to it and fire it off into space, smash it with a sledgehammer or simply throw it in the bin, you decide! All that matters here is that you get rid of that ball.

5. This exercise will instantly release any tension that you may be holding in your body: It's called the 'floppy doll' exercise. It looks a little strange and so I always advise my clients to do this exercise when they are alone or have somewhere that they can go to that is more private:

Stand with your feet slightly apart and your back straight with your arms hanging loosely by your side. When you are ready, slowly lean forward from your waist as far as it feels comfortable for you. Leave your head hanging down. Let your arms hang loose and heavy, gently swaying and stay in this position and feel the tension leaving your body.

In this book, I have bared my soul and spoken to you about Beryl and how she kept me chained in misery and anxiety for so many years. I have also shared with you a few examples of case studies of real clients that I have worked with. We all had one thing in common, and that was that we wanted a happier, more peaceful life within. My clients and I have used the exercises, meditations, and affirmations in this book.

Now that you have used some of the self-help and mindfulness techniques, you will feel what it feels like to be free from anxiety and stress. You have now discovered how wonderful it can be to feel happy and calm and peaceful inside. You can now continue your life in a more positive and healthier way.

Now that you have read this book and understood that a good life matters greatly, you will be able to enjoy every new day and be able to successfully deal with all the challenges that come your way. Your life circumstances may stay the same but how you deal with them can be so different. Everything and everyone has energy, hence **The Law of The Universe** will bring back to you the energy that you are living, as you begin to find life becomes more comfortable and more peaceful for you. Your life will reflect this and more peaceful and more comfortable situations will begin to occur and your life will begin to turn around into something more beautiful and tranquil and your feeling of contentment within will increase.

Put this book down for a moment and take a breath. No matter what your past regrets have been or your worries for the future are, focus on your breathing for a moment or two now and be totally present in the moment. Right now, right at this moment in time, you are safe, you are ok.

As you now experience the feelings of calm and peace where misery once was, take a moment to enjoy this feeling and recognise that you deserve good things, that you deserve a good life.

Clients that I have worked with, who used the tools in this book, are living happier, calmer lives not only in their relationships with others but also in their relationship with themselves.

As you move forward in your life's journey, continue to pick up this book and use your favourite exercises until you get to know them by heart. Carry your favourite affirmations with you and look at them several times a day. Speak them softly or powerfully to yourself. Enjoy the meditations and remember you can email me tamsin@tamsincooper.co.uk for a free audio copy.

I would love to hear how this book has helped you in your journey, everyone has a story and your story will, with the help of this book become less stressful, creating a calmer and happier 'you'!

This Self-Help Book Can Change Your Life
Are you Ready to Make Lasting Changes?

If you read this book you will move from a place of stress or anxiety to a place of calmness and peace.

Almost every leading book on stress and anxiety explains the value of mindfulness but this book goes one step further: it contains a treasure of 40 detailed and easy-to-learn mindfulness techniques that have the power to transform your life.

Also, as a bonus for you in this book, you will find a code that gives you access to download 6 meditations for free that are normally retailed at £60.

Mindfulness is a mystery to most yet many studies have shown how it can easily combat stress, anxiety, and depression.

This book shows you the proof and then step-by-step teaches you the methods that are easy to follow for a happier more fulfilled 'you', and discover a new state of inner peace and joy.

Tamsin Cooper is an International Master Clinical Hypnotherapist specialising in Anxiety and Stress. In her twenty years in practice, she has helped thousands of people make positive changes to their lives. You can watch real-life video testimonials from some of her clients on her YouTube channel **Tamsin Cooper Hypnotherapy** or by visiting her website **www.tamsincooper.co.uk**

Tamsin Cooper offers Hypnotherapy Worldwide

Printed in Great Britain
by Amazon

BRADY G. WILSON is the co-founder of Juice Inc., an organization committed to transforming people, teams, and organizations. Juice exists to energize work environments where employees feel engaged, human energy flourishes, and potential is released. Brady has energized leaders, managers, and front-line workers in many of North America's Fortune 500 companies. His passion for creating breakthroughs for companies has spawned such innovative tools and programs as Pull Conversations™, The Five Drivers of Engagement™, and The Juice Check™. Also the author of the books *Finding the Sticking Point* and *Juice: The Power of Conversation*, Brady lives in Guelph, Ontario.

LOVE AT WORK

ALSO BY BRADY G. WILSON

Juice: The Power of Conversation

Finding the Sticking Point: Increase Sales by Transforming Customer Resistance into Customer Engagement

LOVE AT WORK

Why Passion Drives Performance in the Feelings Economy

BRADY G. WILSON

BPS
books

Published in 2010 by

BPS Books
Toronto and New York
bpsbooks.com
A division of
Bastian Publishing Services Ltd.

ISBN 978-1-926645-16-2 (softcover)
ISBN 978-1-926645-25-4 (hardcover)

Cataloguing-in-Publication Data available from Library and Archives Canada.

Cover design: Gnibel
Text design and typesetting: Casey Hooper Design

Dedicated to my Mother,

Violet Wilson,

my model of love at work

CONTENTS

INTRODUCTION

You want to love people. You probably wouldn't be reading this book if you didn't. But love in the workplace feels subversive. God help your reputation if you blow your cover and people find out you're a loving person. You'll be silenced and sidelined.

A vicious dogma is at loose in the workplace and it has suffocated people's spirits and dehumanized their days.

This dogma is fed by fear and a need for control. It focuses all of its energy on the eradication of one particularly incendiary word. You know this word, but you must pretend not to. The dogma declares, "Love is not allowed at work. Do not speak it. Do not display it."

The word *love* is stigmatized, cheapened, and plundered of its noblest meanings.

Psychoanalysts consider love to be the pinnacle of human self-actualization. It is the developmental yardstick of every great spiritual tradition. Its attainment is our one sure mark of maturity, the

1

antidote to our psychoses. How curious, then, that we permit the practice of love in every sphere of our lives except the one in which we spend the greatest number of our waking hours: the workplace.

Through *Love at Work* I hope to enflame you with a rebel's passion: a rebellion that will embolden you to throw off tradition and love your people. My goal is simple: I want to build a better world. I believe that loving organizations led by loving leaders are the most effective means to achieving that end. My purpose is to energize such organizations: the ones that do good things in the world. But I know that positive change will happen only if leaders build cultures where managers can learn to extend themselves, investing in the highest good of their people, their communities, and their planet.

Throughout this book I'm going to tell you real stories about real leaders and managers who have learned to love their people. My goal is to show you how love trumps logic: how *engaging people's hearts trumps engaging their minds when it comes to sparking discretionary effort.*

In this book you will look at a straightforward definition of love from different angles: *Love is extending yourself to invest in another's highest good.*

You will discover the elemental rule of the feelings economy: *When you meet felt needs, you release the energy that triggers discretionary effort.*

You'll find out that *love is how you grow and expand your orbit of contribution as a human being.*

You will see that *love is just as much about justice as it is about compassion.*

You will learn that love is not a talent that you're born with. *Love is a skill*—and therefore, like any skill, it can be learned and practiced.

You will discover that you already are a loving person. You love in all sorts of ways. The question is: *Are you loving in ways that will build a better world?*

I will tell you practical stories of what love does: how it *believes, pulls, serves, cares, and challenges.*

You not only will witness fellow leaders modeling love, you also will learn how to extract what is important from each of their stories. You will see how you can transform what you learn into your own voice, your own style, and your own way of expressing love at work.

My objective in writing this first edition of *Love at Work* is simple and straightforward: to invite you to share your love at work stories with me and the world. As you read each chapter, ask yourself, "Have I witnessed a leader who does this? Do I have a story that would benefit the business community?"

Introduction

If your answer is yes, send the story to me at bwilson@juiceinc. com. Please let me know whether you wish me to use the real names of the people in your stories.

My hope is that you will find *Love at Work* both enjoyable and beneficial.

With love and respect,

Brady G. Wilson
Juice Inc.

1 | LOVE ENERGIZES RESULTS

Love is the energy source
that fuels spectacular performance.

Picture yourself in your late sixties as the CEO of a family-run facility that produces high-end polar fleece for companies like North Face, L.L. Bean, and Patagonia. It's the mid-nineties and your plant employs three thousand highly paid North American workers. Your competitors, in search of cheaper labor, have moved offshore or down south.

You wake up one morning to find your factory burned to the ground. You stand to receive a $300-million insurance settlement in compensation for your losses. What would you do? Take the money and retire? Take the opportunity to move offshore to reduce your labor costs and increase your profits?

THE MENSCH OF MALDEN MILLS

Aaron Feuerstein faced precisely this dilemma in the days that followed a severe body blow to his business. He got up on the morning of December 11, 1995, to discover that his Malden Mills plant had succumbed to the worst fire Massachusetts had seen in a century. The small town of Lawrence was devastated. Malden Mills was one of the largest employers in an area that was already in a state of desperation.

What did Feuerstein do? And how did his behavior compare with that of other corporate executives in the mid-nineties? Seen in the context of CEOs paying themselves obscene bonuses before filing for bankruptcy and leaving employees' retirement funds in ruins, his behavior was heartening. Seen in the context of CEOs making $50 million a year through aggressive downsizing, cost-cutting, and bailing out in search of cheaper labor, his behavior was astonishing.

Here's how the Website of CBS TV* chronicles Feuerstein's actions:

> "The only thing that went through my mind was, how can I possibly recreate it," says owner Aaron Feuerstein, the third generation of his family to run the mill.

> "I was proud of the family business and I wanted to keep that alive, and I wanted that to survive. But I also felt the responsibility for all my employees, to take care of them, to give them jobs."

He made a decision—one that others in the textile industry found hard to believe. Feuerstein decided to rebuild right there in Lawrence—not to move south or overseas as much of the industry had done in search of cheap labor.

He also made another shocking decision. For the next sixty days, all employees would be paid their full salaries.

I'm wondering why a business leader would do something like this. I'm also wondering what I would have done in the same situation. What would you have done? Says Feuerstein, "I think it was a wise business decision, but that isn't why I did it. I did it because it was the right thing to do."

---

* http://www.cbsnews.com/stories/2003/07/03/60mimutes/main561656.shtm

Who keeps their employees on the payroll for what ended up being three months to the tune of $25 million? When the CBS journalist suggested to Feuerstein that some would see cashing in the $300 million and cashing out the business as the smartest business decision, Feuerstein replied: "And what would I do with it? Eat more? Buy another suit? Retire and die? … No, that did not go into my mind."

Feuerstein kept his promises. Workers picked up their checks for months. He became known as the Mensch of Malden Mills, a businessman who cared more about his workers than his net worth.

Do corporations really have a responsibility to care for their communities? Art Boulay quotes Feuerstein's answer to this question:

> I have a responsibility to the worker, both blue-collar and white-collar … I have an equal responsibility to the community. It would have been unconscionable to put 3,000 people on the streets and deliver a death blow to the cities of Lawrence and Methuen.*

Here's a crucial question: If you do the right thing, do you get great results? Note this comment by Feuerstein:

> Before the fire, that plant produced 130,000 yards a week … A few weeks after the fire, it was up to 230,000 yards.

---

* Boulay, "A Study in Leadership."

Our people became very creative. They were willing to work 25 hours a day.

How many corporate CEOs in today's downsize-crazed companies could ask their employees to double production in a few weeks given no changes in the current plant, much less in temporary plants set up in old warehouses? How many of *your* employees would come through for you if your company needed their help?

What did you notice about Feuerstein's story? Here are a few thoughts that come to my mind. We all know it's important to love our partner. To love our kids is vital. So is loving our parents, our siblings, and our friends. Some leaders even dare to bring love into their careers: loving their customers, loving results, and loving their jobs. But a very select few have ventured into the arena of loving their people.

I think Feuerstein operates in this realm. And I believe his story also suggests this working definition of the word *love*: *Love is extending yourself to invest in another's highest good.* That's what this book is about.

EXTENDING YOURSELF

There's something powerful about a love that really costs you something. In Feuerstein's case, the fiscal and emotional sacrifice was substantial. As you'll see in more detail in the next chapter, love is the process of *extending yourself*. It makes you big.

INVESTING IN OTHERS

Investing in another person is what makes the sacrifice relational. Love at work is not an indiscriminate, arm's-length generosity that scatters goodwill at random; it's a strategic, relational investment in one person or a group of people.

HIGHEST GOOD

This speaks to the motive. Hear the pathos in Feuerstein's statement, "It would have been unconscionable to put 3,000 people on the streets and deliver a death blow to the cities of Lawrence and Methuen." This point will return to nudge and nuzzle us again and again in the chapters to come. Suffice it to say for now that seeking another's highest good demands a level of dialogue that enables us to respond to the true, felt needs of those we are trying to love.

Here is another pivotal thought that emerges from Feuerstein's story: Love is the energy source that fuels spectacular performance. In a very real sense, love energizes work and produces results. A group of employees that doubles production in temporary plants set up in old warehouses demonstrates a significant level of discretionary effort.

There is a profound lesson here, backed up by research conducted by the Corporate Leadership Council: *Leaders who trigger emotional engagement release 400 percent more discretionary effort than those who trigger rational engagement.* Jean Martin, executive director of the CLC, states:

> Emotional commitment is the ever-elusive love of your job and love of your manager or organization ... Our data [have] proven, year after year, that the emotional side of engagement is actually four times more powerful than the rational side when it comes to driving the business impacts we care about ... One specific finding is that when employees move from being disengaged to being highly engaged, their productivity improves 20 percentage points in performance levels.[*]

What's the difference between rational and emotional engagement? Rational engagement meets the needs of the head; emotional engagement meets the needs of the heart. Examples of rational engagement are:

* I understand the strategic objectives of my organization.

* I understand the big picture of how things work here and how I fit into it.

* I understand the expectations my manager has of me.

Examples of emotional engagement are:

---

[*]   https://clc.executiveboard.com/Public/CLCintheNews.aspx

* My leaders listen to me in a way that makes me feel respected.

* I am proud of the purpose of my organization.

* I feel my manager has my back.

Here is something vital for all of us to understand: *When you meet felt needs, you release the energy that triggers discretionary effort.* I bet when Feuerstein announced he would invest his $300 million in his three thousand employees, each of them felt like a hundred thousand bucks. And why not? They *felt* that he believed in them, cared about them, and was willing to serve them.

Rational engagement meets the needs of the head.

Emotional engagement meets the needs of the heart.

Remember, it's what is *felt* that matters most to people. it's what is *felt* that energizes people. It's what is *felt* that unlocks their discretionary effort. Wherever you see love at work, you'll see felt needs being met and energized employees giving their best effort.

Why, when emotional engagement is the trump card, do we lead with the logic card? For years I have been puzzled by a certain phenomenon: I meet one leader in an organization who has brilliant ideas and watertight logic but can't get his ideas implemented. I meet another leader, a guy with half-baked ideas who garners support and moves his agenda forward. How does this happen?

Most often, the first leader is appealing to people's rational engagement. He relies on the strength of his logic to capture people's attention. The second leader taps into people's emotional engagement and walks away with four times the discretionary effort of his logic-driven colleague.

Is rational engagement still critical? Absolutely. It's just not where you want to place your primary focus as a leader. Especially when every unit of effort you spend evoking emotional engagement pays you back in four times the discretionary effort.

The power of emotional engagement is probably not a foreign concept to you. And when you think it through, it's probably not surprising to you that the element that triggers emotional engagement is love. When you love your customers, you inspire your employees. When you love your job, that passion infects everybody. When you love results, you ignite an intensity in performance.

This book is simply adding this vital component to your understanding: *When leaders love their people, they engage their emotions and trigger their deepest intrinsic motivators.*

So love your customers, love your job, love results, and don't ever ignore the love your people part, because they are the ones who enable you to actualize and experience your passion for customers, your job, and results.

Perhaps you can see now why emotional intelligence is so critical to a leader's sustainable success. Emotional engagement is released when a leader has a strong emotional connection with employees. Your IQ is the stake that gets you into the game. But your EQ is what enables you to collect the winnings.

Every unit of effort you spend evoking rational engagement pays you back one unit of discretionary effort. Every unit of effort you spend evoking emotional engagement pays you back four units of discretionary effort. And what triggers emotional engagement? Love. Extending yourself to invest in another's highest good.

The big picture of this book's message may be seen on the following page. As we begin the journey of this book together, let me say: Welcome to the feelings economy, where love energizes results. The process is:

1. Love creates feelings.

2. Feelings release energy.

3. Energy gets results.

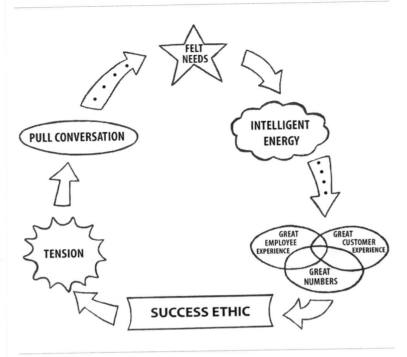

For a short video on this process, go to
http://juiceinc.com/success_ethic.htm

You may be asking yourself, What percentage of my day-to-day activities is focused on unlocking emotional engagement? How can I practically look into what's most important for my employees? Let's turn our attention to those questions now.

2 | LEADERSHIP IN THE FEELINGS ECONOMY

If you want four times the discretionary effort, you have to engage people's emotions.

For years I've been holding up a pack of Dentyne gum and asking people, "When I put a dollar on the counter to buy this gum, what am I buying? Am I buying maltitol, sorbitol, soya bean gum base? What am I really buying?"

Inevitably someone from the audience confidently shouts out, "Fresh breath!"

At that point I say, "With all due respect, I'm not buying fresh breath; I'm buying social acceptance. I want to be able to have a conversation with somebody without having to worry about them thinking, 'Brady, your breath stinks!'"

What's the difference?

Fresh breath is the surface need. But social acceptance is the *felt* need.

When someone goes out to buy an outfit, they're not buying fabric; they're buying a feeling of confidence. When someone buys a Volvo, they are not buying a car; they're buying a feeling of safety.

FEELINGS

I've come to believe that human behavior can best be understood as the attempt to get one's *felt* needs met. In the feelings economy, it's what is *felt* that matters.

It is critical for us to understand this in the workplace. Many leaders manage their people at the level of fresh breath. They offer surface stuff in the hope of motivating their employees. They fail to see that meeting employees' deeper needs is what actually energizes them.

Someone told me a story recently that illustrates this point perfectly. She said her manager tried to recognize his employees by taking them to a Toronto Maple Leafs game.

"And what was the outcome?" I asked.

"Not so good," she replied. "We're all females and most of us are Asians. Hockey means nothing to us."

The score? Fresh breath 1; social acceptance 0.

I wonder what the impact would have been if he'd taken them all out to dinner and then to a play.

Here's what another employee told me:

> My manager keeps coming to me and offering me developmental and educational opportunities. I finally had to tell her, "Listen. I have three kids at home and I'm a single mom. I have a really busy life. I know you're only trying to help me out, but what I really need more than anything else is just to do my job and then go home to be with my kids."

Perceived need? Career and development opportunities. Felt need? Peace of mind that she's being a good mom.

Meeting felt needs is elemental to every relationship in life. A marriage with unmet needs is called divorce. A manufacturing plant with unmet needs is called a strike. A society with unmet needs, a revolution. Two countries with unmet needs, a war. Marshall Rosenberg, the creator of non-violent communication, sums it up nicely: "Every form of blame, criticism and judgment is just a tragic expression of an unmet need."

Everything you do as a manager has the potential to meet a felt need or let one go unmet. Meet a felt need and you release the energy that triggers discretionary effort. Let that need go unmet and you release the energy that triggers cynicism, apathy, and presenteeism (lights on, nobody home).

TAKE THE SIXTY-MINUTE TEST

Picture yourself on the way to work. You're aware that you have a one-hour meeting booked from eleven till noon. Your BlackBerry goes off and you quickly scan the e-mail message: "11 a.m. meeting canceled."

What do you do (after you shout *yes!*)? You now have sixty discretionary minutes you weren't counting on. Do you dive into the pile on your desk, finishing something that will make you 10 percent more productive? Or do you take ten minutes with each of your six direct reports and meet their needs, making each of *them* 10 percent more productive for the day?

How you do this math makes all the difference in the world. Here's the math of the feelings economy.

THE 10% — 400% — 20% EQUATION

* Invest 10 percent of your psychological capital on meeting your employees' felt needs (60 of your 600 minutes spent at work).

* This releases emotional engagement, which unlocks 400 percent more employee effort. (See Corporate Leadership Council study of over 50,000 employees at 59 global organizations.)

* This translates into a 20 percent hike in performance. (Also validated by the CLC study.)

* This drives a great employee experience, a great customer experience, and outstanding financial results.

I see far too many managers get this math all wrong. Instead of investing 10 percent of their time releasing energy in their people, they define themselves by how much stuff they can clear off their desk every day. Few managers can make the shift from "I'm an individual contributor" to "I exist to contribute through others."

I'm not asking you for more time or more energy. I'm asking you to invest 10 percent of your time and energy in a different way. Love at work is a 10 percent shift in:

* What you do.

* How you do it.

* When you do it.

* Why you do it.

You are already expending time and energy finding the right place for every employee. Learn how a 10 percent shift in believing the best of each employee can help you find the right fit for a person: the area where they can operate in a state of flow and feel strong as they execute their duties.

You are already expending time and energy communicating with people. Learn how a 10 percent shift in directness and inquiry can pull discoveries out of people: the kinds of discoveries that energize them to go beyond the call of duty for you and for your customer.

You are already expending time and energy supporting people. Learn how a 10 percent shift can enable you to give them felt support: the kind of support that demonstrates you're managing their success, not just their performance.

You are already expending time and energy recognizing people. Learn how a 10 percent shift in your ability to demonstrate care builds people's sense of worth and creates a strong emotional connection between you and them.

You are already expending time and energy trying to motivate people. Learn how a 10 percent shift in how you challenge people can stretch them in a way that inspires a deep sense of purpose.

In short, your real job is to create the conditions in which your people's felt needs can be met. It is to release emotional energy inside them and set them up to initiate actions that produce great results.

> **Your role is not** to clear off your desk.
>
> **Your role is** to meet your people's felt needs.

The problem is that people's felt needs typically aren't tattooed on their foreheads. How can you sleuth out what's most important to an employee? Here's where love becomes very practical. There is one activity that star managers do that is brilliantly simple and slices right through all the mystery surrounding felt needs: *They ask.*

Working with a shorthand list of core drivers, they simply sit with an employee and say, in effect:

"I think you and I want the same thing: for you to be success-ful in your job. That's good for you, good for the organization, and good for me.

"But I don't want to guess at what you need to feel successful in your role. So I've got a few core drivers here. I'm wondering if you could fill out what's most important for you. I'll fill out what I think is most important for you. Then we'll sit down and compare notes. My goal is to see if we can work together to make sure your core needs are getting met on the job."

We've been helping managers do this with their employees for several years. It takes the mystery right out of managing peo-ple. Based on research conducted by Towers-Perrin, Gallup, Blessing White, Hewitt, Corporate Leadership Council, and many other fine firms, we have distilled a short list of the Five Drivers of Engagement that matter more to employees than anything else in the workplace.

The list is a tool designed to help managers and employees talk about what matters most in the work experience. (You can get more information on the science behind the five drivers by downloading our white paper at http://www.juiceinc.ca/whitepaper.htm.)

Here are the Five Drivers of Engagement, each one framed as a statement that employees wish they could utter at the end of their workday.

"I FIT"

My role is a good match for my talents. My role is a good match for my interests. I fit in well with my team. I feel I belong here. I feel safe in my current role, both emotionally and physically.

"I'M CLEAR"

I'm crystal clear on the outcomes and goals that are expected of me. I'm clear on the big picture and how I contribute to it. I'm clear on how my manager feels about my progress. I feel understood by those around me. I experience no unnecessary friction due to misunderstanding.

"I'M SUPPORTED"

I feel equipped with all the resources I need to succeed: time, training, tools, and systems. My manager has my back, supporting me and going to bat for me when I need it. I have the freedom and authority to do what I'm responsible to do. I'm getting the growth opportunities and challenges that are important to me.

"I'M VALUED"

I feel valued as a person, not as a tool or an asset. I feel recognized and appreciated for my contribution. I feel I am being treated fairly. My leaders listen to me in a way that makes me feel completely understood.

"I'M INSPIRED"

I clearly see the link between my day-to-day activities and the grander purpose of my organization. I am proud of the purpose of my organization. I am being held accountable to achieve great results. My colleagues and leaders walk the talk. The passion of my colleagues inspires me to drive for more aggressive goals.

When these five drivers are met, employees experience a state of well-being that allows their best work to emerge.

A state of being is where people live. It is a pervasive and all-encompassing emotional state. For instance, frustration, worry, and sadness are all emotions, but depression is a state of being. Acceptance and inclusion are emotions, but belonging is a state of being. Look now at the five drivers and the states of being that they create:

Five Drivers	States of Being
"I Fit"	Belonging
"I'm Clear"	Security
"I'm Supported"	Freedom
"I'm Valued"	Significance
"I'm Inspired"	Purpose

In my estimation, a leader's greatest challenge is not supporting, valuing, or inspiring; it is doing these things in a way that
leaves the person *feeling* supported, *feeling* valued, and *feeling*
inspired. There is a massive difference between support and *felt*
support.

I have a friend who lost her husband a few years ago. He was
very well known in the small community in which they lived.
When he died, a virtual avalanche of concern poured in toward
her and her three children. The townspeople intended to be
supportive, but the effect was just the opposite.

If my friend was walking down the street trying to run a few
errands, she was interrupted every few minutes by someone
wanting to know exactly how she was doing. Not only did it
take forever to buy groceries, her limited energy supply was
depleted as she managed the emotions of her well-wishers.

While all this was going on, there was one guy who came to
her house once a week, backed his car up to her driveway, took
out his lawnmower, and cut her grass. He never said a word;
he just cut the grass, then loaded his lawnmower back into the
car and drove away.

What do you suppose her response was to this act of caring? She
would look out through a crack in the curtains and cry with
relief. This, for her, was the essence of felt support. "Thank
goodness. The grass really needs to be cut but I can't figure out
how to start our dumb lawnmower." What she really wanted

and needed was the space to sort out some major decisions and the time to be home with her girls.

Were the others trying to support her? Absolutely. Was it *felt* support? Not really.

Here's my point: Transforming support into *felt* support, value into *felt* value, and clarity into *felt* clarity takes energy, attention, and imagination. There is only one leadership activity that invests that sort of psychological value. That activity is love.

Remember, in the end, it's only what is felt that matters. Why? Because if you want four times the discretionary effort, you have to engage people's emotions. This occurs only when they feel the impact of your love.

Here's the key point: Employee engagement is an inside job. It is emotion driven. Your intent to engage people will not win the day; only your impact will. Few leaders really understand the difference between intent and impact.

Let's shift from work to school for a second to illustrate this point. In her book *The Challenge to Care*, Nel Noddings says to teachers:

> No matter how hard teachers try to care, if the caring is not received by students, the claim "they don't care" has some validity. It suggests strongly that something is very wrong.*

---

* Noddings, p. 15.

This dynamic shows up not only at work and at school but also at home. When Alan Alda was a boy, his dog died. In an attempt to console him, his parents took the dog to a taxidermist and had it stuffed. When they presented it to Alan with its evil, leering grin, it was clear that this expression of "love," though well intended, had missed the mark. Alda's felt need for comfort was left unmet.

I've done a lot of work with parents and their children. When I ask a room full of parents, "How many of you really love your children?" 100 percent of the hands go up. When I ask the children of those parents, "Do you feel loved by your mom and dad?" a surprisingly low percentage of hands go up.

What's missing for many parents is not love itself. It's the ability to demonstrate love so it is felt and received.

NO TO NARCISSISM

Before I go one step further, I need to be very clear about one thing: Love at work is not about feeding people's narcissism. I'm not talking about the kind of love that created a generation of hobbled kids with swollen egos and an over-inflated sense of entitlement. That is the antithesis of love at work.

Twenge and Campbell, authors of *The Narcissism Epidemic*, describe our millennials (born between 1980 and 1995) in stark terms. My view of this crew is more charitable, but I believe there is credibility to these authors' findings. Millennials, they say:

* Grew up with *I Am Special* coloring books and princess parties.

* Enjoyed multi-thousand-dollar Sweet 16 parties and plastic surgery as a graduation present, all in the name of self-esteem.

* Could count on mommy and daddy to fix everything.

* Learned they would never fail as long as they showed up.

This coddling kind of love does not invest itself in the highest good of the recipient. In fact, it sets them up for failure. Those who experienced walloping dollops of this kind of love enter adult life with a lack of ability to:

* Delay gratification.

* Withstand stress to the point of breakthrough and growth.

* Empathize with those experiencing hardship.

* Anticipate others' needs.

* Sacrifice their own needs for the good of others.

In contrast, love at work seeks others' true potential. It challenges them and stretches them to fulfill it—hardships notwithstanding. In essence, we need love at work because it is the antidote to narcissism.

I believe our millennials are drowning in freedom and starving for purpose. Teaching them to love will be transformational for them and for us. We will have to extend ourselves and invest the energy to understand how they see the world. We will have to help them see clearly how they can develop an ever-expanding orbit of contribution that frees them from the smallness of narcissism.

In the feelings economy, there will be significant challenges as well as significant rewards for those who learn to love at work.

3 | WHY LOVE AT WORK?

Wherever you find a culture where
results are humming, values are
working, and people are energized,
you will find love at work.

Have you ever worked for someone like Ryan?

Ryan was a senior manager who kept two fishbowls in his office. In one were goldfish; in the other was a piranha. Ryan asked each of his staff to pick out the goldfish that was most like themselves (the spotted one, the one with deeper color, and so forth). Then, when Ryan was displeased with someone, he asked the person to take his or her goldfish out of the bowl and feed it to the piranha.*

THE FRACTIONALIZER

Most of us have been sold some conventional wisdom about performance that hasn't served us very well. It's bound up in an equation that looks like this:

$$P = T + E + K$$
Performance = Talent + Energy + Knowledge

You'd think you would be guaranteed a good level of performance from an employee who is talented, energized, and knowledgeable. But one critical variable is missing.

We do a lot of work in the field of health care. We often encounter scrub nurses who work in the operating room. They tell us about a nursing colleague who is talented, energized, and knowledgeable yet who makes dumb mistakes when working with a surgeon who is intimidating, threatening, and dismissive.

---

* Peter J. Frost, p. 35.

Why? Because performance = talent + energy + knowledge *divided by* I, *the amount of interference the person is experiencing.* In this case, the nurse's fear of public embarrassment and retaliation fractionalizes her talent, her ability to be energized, and her ability to access her knowledge.

The real performance equation looks like this:

$$P = \frac{T + E + K}{I}$$

Following are just a few of the types of interference people face in the workplace.

INEQUITY

Members of a team who take on more work because others are not pulling their load begin to resent the fact that the manager is not addressing the underperformers. Resentment and cynicism gnaw away at their minds day after day as significant forms of interference that ultimately fractionalize their energy.

LOW EQ

Claude is a CEO with a razor-sharp intellect. He uses it to keep his VPs on their toes in senior team meetings. However, his habit of psychologically undressing and dismantling leaders in front of their peers has kept intelligence from emerging around the leadership table. Intimidation and fear of public embarrassment combine to fractionalize their ability to access their knowledge.

THE SAY/DO GAP

When leaders publicly trumpet the value of honesty by imprinting the word on the mission statement plaque but hide mistakes from customers and employees, their employees become cynical and soon lose their passion for their job.

NEGATIVITY

Major interference occurs inside employees when they are doing so many things right but hear from their manager only when they do something wrong. Research conducted by Gallup revealed that "the number-one reason most Americans leave their jobs is that they don't feel appreciated. In fact, 65% of people surveyed said they got no recognition for good work last year."*

BETRAYAL

Trust is breached and interference increased when an employee shares a vital piece of information with a manager in confidence and later discovers that it was leaked to her co-workers.

---

* Rath and Clifton, p. 31.

HOW INTERFERENCE
FRACTIONALIZES PERFORMANCE

Visualize that scrub nurse who works with an intimidating surgeon. To the extent that she can focus her attention on the critical variables of her job, she is able to stay in the zone and perform at a high level. However, her fear of being publicly embarrassed demands her singular focus. As a result, she is unable to focus her attention on the value-adding components of her job.

Ultimately, because *her need for survival will always trump her need to perform*, her mental energy is diverted to the task of protection versus the task of performance. This dynamic of compensating for unmet emotional needs plays itself out with every form of interference.

When any one of the five core emotional needs is unmet, energy will be consumed needlessly.

* When an employee feels he doesn't fit in with the team, he will waste energy posturing and seeking to be accepted.

* When someone isn't clear about her manager's expectations, she will consume needless energy over-delivering on non-value-adding tasks.

* When an employee doesn't feel his manager has his back and supports him, he will spend too much energy in CYA activity.

* When an employee doesn't feel valued, she
  will consume needless energy flaunting her
  accomplishments in an attempt to be noticed.

* When someone doesn't feel inspired about his
  work, he will consume needless energy chasing after
  pursuits that seem closer to his ideology.

We compensate for these feelings in order to get through our day, but the depletion of mental energy always destroys our focus and truncates our performance.

The performance equation above is a lens. Look through it to determine the impact of any decision or action you are about to take.

Let's say you are about to send out a mass e-mail to two hundred and twenty people to let them know that they are being terminated. You can ask yourself, "Will this way of telling them create interference or will it remove it?" If you think the e-mail might create interference, you may wish to rethink your decision and take a different approach.

Does this sound like an unbelievable example? Unfortunately leaders have done just this sort of thing all too often.

WHERE DOES INTERFERENCE COME FROM?

What is it that prompts behaviors like bullying, rumor-mongering, CYA (cover your ass), posturing and hyper-cynicism?

What do they all have in common?

Every one of them may well be a tragic expression of an unmet need.

* The person who bullies often lacks fit and belonging.

* The person who feeds the rumor mill often lacks clarity and certainty.

* The person who engages in CYA activities often lacks the support and freedom that comes from feeling "my manager has my back."

* The person who is posturing often lacks value and significance.

* The person who is cynical often lacks inspiration.

This gives us a new lens through which to interpret people's actions. Take a good look behind any unproductive behavior and you may find an unmet need. Adopting this mindset can serve you in two ways:

1. You'll stop seeing people as opponents and begin seeing them as neighbors with unmet needs. (See the "Love believes the best" section of chapter 6.)

2. You'll discover the shortest route to removing interference: helping people get their needs met.

Unmet needs—lack of security, lack of control, feelings of being misunderstood—are the perfect breeding grounds for fear, and it's fear that fuels toxic behaviors. Here is a big reason why we need love at work: *Love pushes out fear.* Intelligence doesn't push out fear. Talent doesn't. Nor does skill. Love is the only thing powerful enough to push fear out of a relationship. And science provides the reason for this.

> Even though you can be presented with evidence that something is true, you won't really believe it unless you feel that it is true. It may be reasonable, logical, scientifically proven or just plain common sense, but you won't believe it unless your brain's limbic system (the seat of your emotions) allows you to feel that it is true. Your emotions are not separate, but rather enmeshed in the neural networks of reason in your mind. The limbic system provides you with feelings that tell you what is real, true and important.*

> **Intelligence, talent, and skill** do not push out fear.
>
> **Love** pushes out fear.

So here's what love does: It causes people to feel that certain things are true. They hear: "You belong." "You are valued." "I will support you." When feeling is added to these messages, the

---

* Caroline Leaf, *Who Switched Off My Brain?*

person can believe them. At that point, it will be much easier for them to believe that your intentions toward them can be trusted.

ENERGY LEFT OVER

I believe every employee deserves to have energy left over at the end of the day: energy for their partner—enjoying a great relationship; energy for their kids—coaching that soccer team; energy for their community—volunteering on that board. It's not okay for employees to go home from work, walk in the door, and flop down on the couch with nothing left over for the other important spheres of their life.

Here's what we at Juice have discovered: Wherever you find a culture where results are humming, values are working, and people are energized, you will find love at work.

Leaders: As cultural architects you play a profound role here. If you promote or even just permit a culture of results at any cost, you deny your employees the opportunity to self-actualize. The results-at-any-cost culture leaves no time or energy for employees to identify or satisfy a co-worker's unmet needs.

As I said above, unmet needs manifest themselves in fear and forms of interference: the types of interference that produce low morale and burnout and that ironically short-circuit long-term results.

We've all seen enough pain in the workplace. We've watched competent, intelligent people be dismantled and degraded to the point that they second-guess their decisions. We've seen dignified men and women embarrassed and unable to hold back the tears. Max De Pree illustrates this in his book *Leading Without Power.*

> I don't tell this story with any pride, but some time ago when I was still CEO at Herman Miller, the office furniture company where I worked for most of my life, I got a call from a salesman whom I had known for more than ten years. "I'm calling you," he said, "because we've been friends for a long time, and I just want you to know I'm going to work for the competition." This came as a real surprise because I had always thought of this man as a person with a fine future in the company. Naturally, I was interested to know why he was leaving Herman Miller. He said, "I'm leaving because I have a broken heart. I made a mistake eight years ago and nobody will forget it.*

That's sad! Because we have not practiced and demanded love in the workplace, selfish people have inflicted cruelty and injustice on others. This has left people dehumanized and depleted of energy. In my mind, love at work is not just an issue of compassion, it's an issue of justice.

Left to ourselves, we gravitate to selfishness rather than toward

---

* De Pree, p. 17.

extending ourselves to invest in others. This produces issues of control, isolation, mistrust, fear, domination, unhealthy competition, backbiting, and suspicion.

Why practice love in the workplace? Because if we don't, we dehumanize others, unraveling the very fabric of their lives and our own.

We don't know the full extent of the suffering exacted by loveless workplaces, but we do know that work-related stress is skyrocketing and crippling productivity. We also know that toxic work environments are increasingly contributing to mental illness. We can only guess at the impact of loveless workplaces on our immune systems, heart disease, and our ability to fight off cancer.

THE FORBIDDEN WORD

Visualize the face of your best friend. Is there anything you wouldn't do to help her if it was in your power to do so?

What about your favorite sibling? How much of your time and energy would you give to listen to him and understand him if he was going through a rough patch?

If you are a parent, what about your kids? Is it fair to say you'd go to almost any length to do something that would serve their greater good?

Just think about this. You are willing to invest amazing amounts of psychological capital in these people in terms of time, money, and mental and emotional energy. There is a word that sums up all these investments: love.

Love is the one great affect that holds relationships together. In fact, *love is the element that makes relationships work.*

As I look at all the behaviors above, I'm struck by the simple thought that we need more of them in the workplace. You can be grateful that you experience them with your friends, your siblings, your partner, and your children. But wouldn't it be humanizing and fulfilling to experience them where you spend the greatest number of your waking hours?

What would life be like for you if you had leaders who went out of their way to understand your reality? Co-workers who anticipated and met your needs? Managers who did everything in their power to make you successful? What if you had leaders who were passionate about and loved their people? My guess is that you would go home at the end of the day fully energized.

I've been talking to groups of people about the notion of love at work for a year or so now. I'm startled by how strongly people respond to this simple but revolutionary idea. I guess people are ready for a more humanized work environment.

For love to take up lodgings in our offices and factories, two pervasive paradigms need to be shifted.

THE GREAT SEPARATION

The first paradigm is that love and work are two entirely separate things.

But what if it was okay to demonstrate *loyalty* at home but punishable if you demonstrated it at work?

What if *empathy* was condoned at home but condemned at work?

How would the workplace fare if these and other virtues were allowed only within the confines of our homes?

Such a world would be unthinkable. Why, then, do we accept such a duality as normal when it comes to love? Why accept that it's okay to practice love at home but not in the workplace? What brand of dualism has enticed us to think that *work* should be "business only"?

THE GREAT CONFUSION

The second paradigm that must shift is the confusion of love with sex or romance. This confusion strips love of its noblest meanings: commitment, loyalty, sacrifice, and compassion. The very thing we're starving for has been rendered irrelevant and useless in the workplace.

TWELVE REASONS WE NEED LOVE AT WORK

Because ...

1. Otherwise narcissism, control, domination, unhealthy competition, selfishness, isolation, suspicion, and mistrust will dominate our work–life experience.

2. Leadership without love dehumanizes and trivializes people.

3. Justice is possible in the workplace only through love.

4. Love releases energy, and employees deserve to have energy left over at the end of the day for their partners, their kids, and their communities.

5. Love is the only antidote to our individualism, consumerism, and narcissism.

6. As substantive research shows, loving relationships are one of the vital cures to our current epidemics of mental illness, heart disease, and cancer.

7. Love unlocks emotional engagement, the source of discretionary effort that produces spectacular results.

8. Love grows us into mature human beings able to create a better world.

9. Love scratches our itch to make a difference through our work.

10. Love achieves mastery, since you cannot master anything without passion.

11. Love enables us to understand each other.

12. Love can create a sustainable planet.

Interference—the great fractionalizer—is out to destroy your work experience and that of your employees. As a leader in the feelings economy you can run interference on interference by meeting the felt needs of your employees.

Something interesting happens to leaders in this process: They get bigger. Let's find out how that happens.

4 | LOVE MAKES YOU GROW

Mastering the skill of love in relationships is the most important activity you will ever engage in.

Is love a talent you're born with or a skill you learn? Are some born with the love gene and others without it?

LOVE IS A SKILL

I believe love is a skill. If it is, then like any skill it can be acquired. And if it is a skill to be acquired, we need to both learn about it and practice it. (Erich Fromm developed this concept of love as a skill in his book *The Art of Loving*; you'll hear more from him in later chapters.)

Where did you learn to love? Perhaps your parents corrected you on behaviors that were unloving. Perhaps a teacher commented, "That was a very loving thing to do." Most of what you learned about love you probably learned unconsciously, simply picking it up from others. You watched how your parents treated each other and you silently drew your conclusions regarding what love is like. You derived further clues about love as you watched the interactions of other authority figures, teachers, coaches, and older siblings.

Some of what you learned about love has served your relationships. Some has hindered or even destroyed them. Since mastering the skill of love in relationships is the most important activity you will ever invest in, learning the skill of love is a good use of time. And since you spend half your waking life engaged in work, it makes sense to learn and practice love in your work relationships.

WHAT MAKES YOU BIG?

M. Scott Peck unpacks the concept of human enlargement in his book *The Road Less Traveled*. Peck writes of the psychological concept called cathexis: "When we are attracted to, invest in and commit to an object outside ourselves" we actually cathect it. That is, "we psychologically incorporate a representation of that object into ourselves." In the process of cathexis, we extend the boundaries of our personhood by stretching out toward the object of our love, "whose growth we wish to nurture."*

Mary-Catherine loves her garden. When she takes a break at work, she pulls out her Lee Valley catalogue and studies the gardening section. On rainy days at home she sketches out some plans for her garden. She has incorporated the garden within her, and by this incorporation her self has become enlarged. She is not just Mary-Catherine; she is Mary-Catherine with a garden growing inside her.

Those of us who are parents have experienced this first-hand. For example, I am not just a man: I am a man with children and grandchildren living inside me. Through cathexis—being attracted to, investing in, and committing to the objects of my love—I have become a bigger person.

In short, love is what makes you grow.

---

* Peck, p. 98.

If love makes us grow, think of the size of Mother Theresa's soul. She cathected thousands inside herself. In contrast, think of the size of Howard Hughes' soul.

The concept of cathexis is well expressed in our definition of love: *Love is extending yourself to invest in another's highest good.*

When you extend yourself, you become a bigger leader. You literally become magnanimous. The word *magnanimous* has an interesting set of roots. It comes from the Latin *magnus* = great, and *animus* = soul. A leader with a great soul is someone who is attracted to, invested in, and committed to the highest good of her employees. In short, a great leader is one with great employees living inside her.

Do you want to be big on the inside?

Love is the answer. It helps us develop into big, mature human beings capable of contributing to the world's greater good. Your partner, your kids, your siblings, your friends, your neighbors, and your co-workers are all part of the curriculum of love that life has invited you to learn.

Sacrifice is embedded in the very DNA of love. Because of this, love is the antidote to our society's three most deadly diseases. As I extend myself to others, I am healed of individualism. As I invest in my world, I am healed of consumerism. As I seek others' highest good, I am healed of narcissism.

Love is a powerful antidote to individualism, consumerism, and narcissism.

WE ALL LOVE

By now you may be asking yourself, "How do I stack up in the love department? Am I a loving person?"

I have an answer for you. You are a loving person. You love all sorts of things. Whenever you extend yourself to invest in the highest good of someone or something—that's love.

I often extend myself to invest in the highest good of my customers. So by the definition above, I love my customers.

My neighbor Jim extends himself to invest in the highest good of his Harley. He loves his motorcycle.

Kelly extends herself to invest in marathon training. She loves running.

Whatever you extend yourself to serve, you love.

Love is the selection process that determines what:

* You will do and what you will not do.

* You value and what you throw away.

* You seek after and what you spurn.

* You will devote your time to.

* You will ignore.

The question is not, How can I be a more loving person? You are already a loving person. You love all sorts of things.

The question is, How can I love the things that build a better world?

Your marriage suffers when your spouse feels you love yourself more than you love her.

Your family suffers when your kids feel you love your career more than you love them.

Your business suffers when your customers feel you love your processes more than you love serving them.

We do love. The question is: What do we love? And how do we know what we should love right now, in this moment?

The answer is not as simple as: Don't love things—love people. You *do* love your old Gibson Hummingbird guitar, and if my definition of love holds any water, you should. By all means, extend yourself to invest in its highest good. Polish it, store it at the proper humidity level so it doesn't crack, and don't let your four-year-old shred it with a bread tag.

But if you don't know when to put your Gibson down and listen to your wife's concerns about the colleague who's trying to assassinate her career at work, then she's going to feel you love your Gibson more than you love her. That will not be good for your love life.

And if you go ballistic when your teenager spills hot chocolate in your SUV, he may not care to hang with you.

I remember helping a friend move. The ramp of the moving truck was very slick and I slipped and hurt myself. My friend came running over to express his concern—for his dresser. He began running his hands over the wood to see if any damage had been done. The message was clear: I love my furniture more than I love you.

THE LOVE TEST

If you want to find out what you love, answer the following five questions.

1. What do you make sacrifices for and spend your discretionary time on?

2. What do you get animated and passionate about in conversation?

3. What do you most respect and admire?

4. What will you protect at any cost?

5. What do you "polish, prize, and pursue"?

Loving people enlarges our soul more than loving things. Perhaps that's because people are harder to love than things. Loving a person demands that you extend yourself further and invest yourself more deeply. Extending yourself to invest in your cottage has a pretty linear form of payback to it. The cause-and-effect relationship of investing in people is trickier to track. It takes real belief.

So love things, love ideals, and excel at loving people. Most of all, learn to detect what life is calling you to love in the moment and focus your attention on that.

5 | WHAT LOVE DOES

Valjean walked out the
bishop's door twice: the first as a
reprobate, leaving devastation in
his wake, and the second as
a saint, ready to build a better world
for everyone he touched.

To create an experiential connection for you with what love does, I'd like to tell you a story from Victor Hugo's classic novel *Les Misérables.*

THE PURPOSE OF LOVE

"Do I crush his skull or just take the silverware and run?" This is what raged through the mind of Jean Valjean as he stood poised over the bishop's bed with an iron bar in his hand. Valjean had just been discharged from his lengthy prison sentence: nineteen years as a galley slave for stealing a loaf of bread to feed his sister's starving family.

He now faced a crisis point: murder and rob the kind bishop who had taken him in when no one else would give him lodgings or steal but spare his life.

Something about the bishop's peacefulness caused Valjean to stay his hand. He scooped up the silverware and made good his escape.

In the morning, as the bishop was eating his breakfast, he was interrupted by a knock on the door. Three gendarmes entered, dragging Valjean by the collar.

Before a word could be spoken, the old bishop made his way

---

* Quotes in this chapter are from Victor Hugo, *Les Misérables,* translated by Bennett A. Cerf and Donald S. Klopfer. New York: The Modern Library, 1931.

over to Valjean and said, "Ah there you are! I am glad to see you. But! I gave you the candlesticks also, which are silver like the rest, and would bring two hundred francs. Why did you not take them along with your plates?"

Jean Valjean opened his eyes and looked at the bishop with an expression which no human tongue could describe.

"Monseigneur," said the brigadier, "then what this man said was true? We met him. He was going like a man who was running away, and we arrested him in order to see. He had this silver."

"And he told you," interrupted the bishop, with a smile, "that it had been given him by a good old priest with whom he had passed the night. I see it all. And you brought him back here? It is all a mistake."

"If that is so," said the brigadier, "we can let him go."

"Certainly," replied the bishop.

The gendarmes released Jean Valjean, who shrank back:

"Is it true that they let me go?" he said in a voice almost inarticulate, as if he were speaking in his sleep.

"Yes! You can go. Do you not understand?" said a gendarme.

"My friend," said the bishop, "before you go away, here are your candlesticks; take them."

He went to the mantelpiece, took the two candlesticks, and brought them to Jean Valjean . . .

Jean Valjean was trembling in every limb. He took the two candlesticks mechanically, and with a wild appearance.

"Now," said the Bishop, "go in peace. By the way, my friend, when you come again, you need not come through the garden. You can always come in and go out by the front door. It is closed only with a latch, day or night."

Then turning to the gendarmes, he said:

"Messieurs, you can retire." The gendarmes withdrew.

Jean Valjean felt like a man who was about to faint.

The bishop approached him, and said, in a low voice:

"Forget not, never forget that you have promised me to use this silver to become an honest man."

Jean Valjean, who had no recollection of this promise, stood confounded. The bishop had laid much stress upon these words as he uttered them. He continued, solemnly:

"Jean Valjean, my brother: you belong no longer to evil, but to good. It is your soul that I am buying for you. I withdraw it from dark thoughts and from the spirit of perdition, and I give it to God!"

Love has a purpose: It wants to give a gift. The gift is the feelings created in the one loved. Love harnesses the kinetic energy of powerful actions to accomplish this.

Here is what love does.

LOVE BELIEVES THE BEST

First of all, *love believes the best*. Love has an eye for potential— in this case it looked beyond Valjean's current self and spotted the better self hidden within. Love sees the true potential of the person and says, "I want to actualize the purpose lying dormant within this Valjean fellow."

The conversation between the bishop and Valjean at dinner is exquisite. Allow me to take you back to the previous night to give you a glimpse of the bishop's belief in Valjean.

"Monsieur, sit down and warm yourself: we are going to take supper presently, and your bed will be made ready while you sup."

At last the man quite understood; his face, the expression of which till then had been gloomy and hard, now

expressed stupefaction, doubt, and joy, and became absolutely wonderful. He began to stutter like a madman.

"True? What! You will keep me? you won't drive me away?
A convict? You call me *Monsieur* and don't say 'Get out,
dog!' as everybody else does . . ."

While he was talking, the bishop shut the door, which he
had left wide open.

Madame Magloire brought in a plate and set it on the table.

"Madame Magloire," said the bishop, "put this plate as
near the fire as you can." Then turning towards his guest,
he added: "The night wind is raw in the Alps; you must
be cold, monsieur."

Every time he heard this word monsieur, with his gently sol-
emn, and heartily hospitable voice, the man's countenance
lighted up. *Monsieur*, to a convict, is a glass of water to a man
dying of thirst at sea. Ignominy thirsts for respect . . .

"This is the home of no man, except him who needs an
asylum. I tell you, who are a traveller, that you are more
at home here than I; whatever is here is yours. What need
have I to know your name? Besides, before you told me,
I knew it."

The man opened his eyes in astonishment:

"Really? You knew my name?'

"Yes," answered the bishop, "your name is my brother."

The bishop did not see Jean Valjean the thief, he saw Jean Valjean the gentleman. He did not see Jean Valjean the convict, he saw Jean Valjean the philanthropist. He did not see Jean Valjean the outcast, he saw Jean Valjean the brother.

And the power of belief has a singular effect on its recipient: he feels, "I am not a misfit. I am not disqualified. I fit here—I belong."

LOVE PULLS

Next, *love pulls out the highest good.* It seeks to draw out and understand the reality of a person. It then does its best to pull that person into its own reality. It goes even further by working with the person to pull out the bigger reality: the highest good inherent in the situation or the person.

The bishop looked at Valjean intently and began to inquire deeply into his world.

"You have seen much suffering?"

"Oh, the red blouse, the ball and chain, the plank to sleep on, the heat, the cold, the galley's crew, the lash, the double chain for nothing, the dungeon for a word,—even when sick in bed, the chain. The dogs, the dogs are happier! nineteen years! and I am forty-six, and now a yellow passport. That is all."

When the bishop had understood and reflected back his understanding of Valjean's prior plight, he began to share about relatives of his who had businesses in the area Valjean was traveling to. The two became animated as the bishop began to paint a picture of a better life for Valjean.

This is a wonderful vignette of how love conducts itself in conversation: it leaves the person with a sense of *clarity* they may have never experienced before.

LOVE SERVES

Next, *love serves the success of others.* When Valjean was dragged back into the bishop's home by the gendarmes the next morning, the bishop immediately sized the situation up and identified how he would serve Valjean. Dispelling the suspicion of the gendarmes with a word, he went beyond acquittal, searching for a way to equip Valjean with gifts that would ensure his success.

Those who serve always love to give. For this bishop, the silverware simply would not be enough; Valjean must have the candlesticks as well. By the time Valjean left the bishop's presence, he would have a strong sense not just of support but of *felt* support. The two can be as different as night and day.

LOVE CARES

Next, *love cares for the worth of others.* It cares enough to demonstrate the person's worth with visible expressions of respect and honor.

> "By the way, my friend, when you come again, you need not come through the garden. You can always come in and go out by the front door . . . "

The bishop is impressing on Valjean, "I cherish you. I value you. I prize our friendship. My home is now your home." He goes beyond the invitation and, in a profound act of care, purges Valjean's reputation by reinterpreting his crime of breaking through the garden wall as the inadvertent slip-up of an absent-minded friend who should have used the front door.

In all of this, the bishop is imprinting Valjean with a strong sense of value and significance.

LOVE CHALLENGES

Finally, *love challenges others to stretch.* Love takes a stand for the other's success and squarely declares its intentions. Valjean had no conception of how great he could become. The bishop challenges him in a way that will be impossible for him to forget or ignore.

In the final analysis, love is willing to extend itself to invest in

> **When love has its way,** people are inspired with purpose.

another's highest good. Valjean's encounter with the bishop is a seed, a starting-point from which his life will emerge and take its place in the world. At the end of it all, when love has had its way, Valjean will feel *inspired with purpose* in a rare and potent way because he has become all he could become.

Imagine the powerful feelings going on inside Valjean during these encounters: "I fit, I'm clear, I'm supported, I'm valued, and I'm inspired." Now we can see the connection between love's actions and the five drivers they satisfy.

Love's Actions	The Five Drivers of Engagement
Love Believes	"I Fit"
Love Pulls	"I'm Clear"
Love Serves	"I'm Supported"
Love Cares	"I'm Valued"
Love Challenges	"I'm Inspired"

And these Five Drivers produce results. Remember:

1. Love creates feelings.

2. Feelings release energy.

3. Energy produces results.

Just how does this work? When someone believes in you, you feel the energy that comes from belonging. What do you most naturally do as a result? You initiate toward others and include them. *Love just got multiplied.*

When someone pulls instead of pushes you and you feel completely clear, what do you most naturally do? You communicate. *Love just got multiplied.*

Emotional engagement releases discretionary effort and causes people to initiate. This is how your love multiplies itself to build a better world.

Jean Valjean's life displays and illustrates this dynamic. The feelings generated from his defining experience with the bishop would energize him to found a factory to provide for hundreds, care for Fantine in her final hours, adopt and nurture Cosette to adulthood, support a rag-tag group of students in their struggle for liberty, and dispense a mysterious mercy to a cold, calculating Javert.

But this is not the story of Valjean alone; this is the story of history. Think of what love has energized people to do. For love of their homeland, soldiers have flung themselves headlong against the machines of tyranny. For love of a woman, men have risked life, limb, fortune, and reputation. For love of an ideal, visionaries have withstood prison, torture, and death.

In the next five chapters you will see how believing, pulling, serving, caring, and challenging release the kind of energy that produces results. For now, have a look at the following visual of how great leaders demonstrate these five actions in very practical ways.

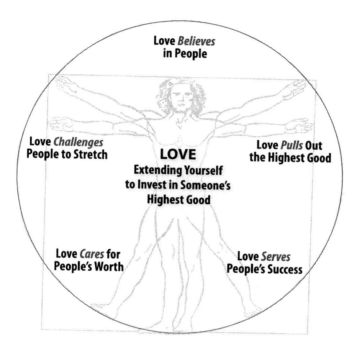

1. The loving leader believes the best in a person, discovering potential waiting to be actualized.

2. She pulls out the highest good: the concrete action that life is asking from this employee—the action they both agree will create fivefold success for the employee, the organization, the team, the customer, and the manager.

3. She then serves their success by clearing away interference and building the conditions that enable the employee to enter into a flow state.

4. As the employee takes action, the leader cares for their worth by affirming intentions and recognizing successes.

5. Although the leader affirms the employee's intentions, she also challenges the impact of the employee's actions.

The life of Jean Valjean had a tremendous impact. But the difference between what the impact was and what it would have been without the bishop's act of love is staggering. Valjean walked out the bishop's door twice: the first as a reprobate, leaving devastation in his wake, and the second as a saint, ready to build a better world for everyone he touched.

Be like the bishop. Love your employee so thoroughly that he walks out your door as the second man, not the first: ready to spend his discretionary effort on building a better world. The difference you can make in an employee's impact is greater than you can know.

Let's move forward to discover the practical things you can do to engage in love at work.

6 | LOVE BELIEVES IN PEOPLE

Love is believing that there
is a highest good for each person
in every situation: a concrete,
act of service that life
is requesting of them.

Imagine yourself suffering severe chest pains from angina. You can't climb the stairs on your own without resting halfway up. You can't walk down the street. You can't make love to your partner.

If your doctor told you, "You have to change your lifestyle or die," would you change? What do you think your odds would be of sustaining a lifestyle change?

AN INABILITY TO CHANGE

The odds are 9 to 1 against you. Alan Deutschman, in his book *Change or Die*, says the odds are against your making and sustaining a lifestyle change. Repeated studies show that after suffering angina and enduring the pain of bypass surgery or angioplasty, 90 percent of heart patients go back to their former lifestyle. In a few years, the bypass grafts clog up. Because of this inability to change lifestyles, only 3 percent of bypass and angioplasty operations prevent the heart attacks that patients are heading toward.

Yet there is an approach, championed by Dr. Dean Ornish, that stands in stark contrast to the "change or die" threat of physicians. And Ornish's treatment is so successful that after graduating from the program and being measured at the three-year mark, "77 percent of the participants had changed their lifestyles so thoroughly that they had safely avoided the need for heart surgery."[*]

---

[*] Deutschman, p. 50.

Wouldn't you love to be able to harness the dynamic that is producing those kinds of results?

We'll come back to Ornish's program in a moment, but first let's look at people in an entirely different sector of society: criminals. They achieve better rates of change than heart patients, but only marginally. In 2002, the largest study of recidivism ever conducted in the United States revealed that "30 percent of former inmates were arrested within six months, and 67.5 percent of them were rearrested within three years."*

But once again there is an approach that is yielding vastly different results. A feisty, four-foot-eleven Dr. Mimi Silbert runs a program called Delancey Street, in San Francisco. Her program takes "drug-addicted, violent, unskilled, psychopathic criminals and hires them to work at an entrepreneurial company with a reputation for customer service."**

And she uses this groundbreaking approach to

> reshape them into law-abiding, sober, peaceful, caring, cooperative, skilled workers ... After staying at Delancey for four years, most of the residents graduate and go out on their own into the greater society. Nearly 60 percent of the people who enter the program make it through and sustain productive lives on the outside.***

---

* Deutschman, p. 5.
** Deutschman, p. 68.
*** Deutschman, pp. 68 and 7.

When you stack these facts up against the conventional penal system, this level of change grabs your attention: six out of ten living productive lives versus six out of ten returning to crime and then to prison.

There is one powerful key that lies at the heart of the results that Ornish and Silbert are achieving: the conviction that *belief in the person unlocks the change process.*

Let me unpack this concept. There is an unfortunate dynamic in the physician–patient relationship: Generally speaking, physicians don't believe that their patients will change. This belief plays itself out in untold numbers of ways throughout the health-care system.

Dr. Ornish takes the opposite approach. His heart patients engage with psychologists, meditation coaches, yoga instructors, dietitians, chefs, and fellow participants in a program in which one common element infuses the process: *belief in the person's ability to change.*

If physicians have a tough time believing that patients can change, what sort of struggles do you think criminologists have believing that criminals can change? Unfortunately, the cynicism and unbelief run deep.

But Dr. Silbert produces stunning results by creating an environment infused with the belief that criminals can change. The person who can read at the sixth grade level can teach the person who reads at the second grade level. Each one learns how to believe in another's ability to change and grow. And when residents believe that everyone can change, they hold one another accountable in transforming ways.

> Residents care for and take responsibility for one another. They kick out anyone who uses drugs, drinks alcohol, or resorts to threats or violence. Although most of them are illiterate when they first arrive, the ex-cons help one another earn their high school equivalency degrees, and they all learn at least three marketable skills. Together they run the top-rated moving company in the Bay area, a thriving upscale restaurant, a bookstore-café, and a print shop ... While taxpayers spend $40,000 a year to support a single prison inmate, Delancey supports itself with profits from its businesses. It never takes money from the government.[*]

The longstanding results of Drs. Ornish and Silbert broadcast a simple message: Belief is more powerful than we imagine. And as you read on, you will discover how belief causes people to flourish and thrive.

BELIEVE THE BEST

A specific type of person is represented by each of the following statements:

---

[*]   Deutschman, introduction.

* Twenty-one of the first twenty-three astronauts were this type of person.

* Two-thirds of those on the Who's Who list were this type of person.

* Fifty-five percent of Supreme Court Justices were this type of person.

* Two-thirds of all entrepreneurs are this type of person.

* Forty-five percent of female world leaders between 1960 and 1999 were this type of person.

If you guessed first-borns, you are right on the money. Considering the fact that they represent only 35 percent of all children, first-borns have a disproportionately powerful impact.

How is this phenomenon explained? According to behavioral psychologist Thomas K. Connellan, the answer lies not in genetics but in how parents treat their first-borns. He says we focus on three specific things with our first-borns that we ease up on with our subsequent children:

1. We have higher expectations of them.

2. We give them more responsibility.

3. We give them more feedback.*

---

* Connellan, *Bringing Out the Best in Others!*

79

WE EXPECT MORE

It's just a given in our minds that our first-born will win the spelling bee, be elected to the student council, and pursue studies at a great university.

WE GIVE MORE RESPONSIBILITY

It's the first-borns we give money to and say, "Now you take care of your little sisters. Buy everyone an ice cream cone and bring back the change."

WE GIVE MORE FEEDBACK

We take more pictures of our first-borns, have more pictures taken of them, attend more of their engagements, and give them more help with their homework.

Now the point of all this is not to make you depressed if you're not a first-born but to help you discover how to create first-born conditions: the conditions that make others successful, no matter what their birth order.

What do these three behaviors have in common? *Belief.* When you believe in someone you expect the best, offer responsibility, and give feedback. In short, belief builds the conditions for people to flourish like a first-born.

Peter J. Frost shares a great illustration of this in his book *Toxic Emotions at Work*.

> A consultant was conducting a high-pressure, two-day seminar for a group of senior managers. At the end of the first day, it was clear to everyone that it was not going very well. Feeling despondent and at a loss about how to proceed, he was gathering up his notes when the CEO came over, put his hand on the consultant's shoulder, and said: "This is a game of halves. I'm sure you will do just fine in the second half tomorrow." That simple remark restored the consultant's confidence to the point that after making several adjustments to the seminar and working long into the night, he delivered a highly successful session the next day.*

Do you put your hand on people's shoulder and say this type of thing? Believing the best actualizes the potentialities that lie hidden within people.

"WE'RE AT THAT POINT"

Two internal candidates applied for the spot left by CEO John Ryan of Farm Credit Canada (FCC). John's tenure had created a new and powerfully effective FCC—an FCC that would be a privilege to lead.

---

* Frost, p. 21.

Greg Stewart had headed up Operations as COO. He had a reputation as someone who wanted to make a difference to customers and the agriculture industry. He drove for results and efficiency and got things done—a trait that would be essential to sustaining and growing FCC's culture.

Kellie Garrett had worked closely with John in his journey to transform FCC in her capacity as a Senior VP with responsibility for business strategy, knowledge management, and communication. She had immense respect for John. Against her better judgment, she applied for the better position. John had encouraged her to do so.

Kellie told me how things went down.

"When Greg was chosen, I was okay about it because I didn't expect to get the job. But after a restructuring I didn't agree with, I felt crushed and interpreted it as a sign. I went into his office, and said, 'This is too weird for me and probably for you, too. So just pay me to go away and I'll say good things.'

"Greg looked at me and said, 'I don't want you to go away. What would it take for you to stay?' "

Kellie and Greg had a long conversation, which she recalls as very emotional on her part. "At the end of it, he said, 'I promise that there will come a point where you will love working for me even more than you loved working for John Ryan.'

"I ended up staying. Last month Greg gave me my performance appraisal. He spent an hour giving me numerous, highly specific examples of my performance that signaled to me just how much he was in touch with my contribution. Then he spent another hour walking me through the very specific ways that he believed I could add more value and offered concrete examples of how I could do so.

"When he was done, I told him, 'You said there would come a point when I would love working with you more than I loved working with John. Well, *we're at that point.*'"

How many new CEOs keep their arch-contender around? Who wants to take that kind of risk? Greg Stewart extended himself to invest in Kellie's highest good, and more than two years later, Kellie wouldn't have it any other way.

I'm sure many factors played into Greg's choice, but high on the list was believing the best. He saw talents and potential in Kellie that he wanted to actualize for her highest good and the highest good of his organization. Believing that your previous competitor can turn the corner and be your trusted ally—that takes a lot of soul.

And Kellie had to believe the best of Greg, too. Believing that your previous competitor can treat you fairly as your boss—that takes a lot of trust.

On the most pragmatic level, believing the best means finding the fit for the employee: the role that's a perfect fit for their wiring (passions and interests) and their talents.

GOT A SOUL?

Does a rock have a soul? Does a turnip? A cocker spaniel? Does a human?

A chunk of limestone does not seek the growth of another being. Neither does a turnip. As far as we can tell, minerals and vegetables have no drive to seek the preservation and growth of others. A cocker spaniel, on the other hand, does exhibit this drive. She cares for and protects beings outside her own scope of concern. Humans take this trait to far more sophisticated levels.

Mihaly Csikszentmihalyi offers these thoughts on the concept of soul:

> No matter how complex a system is, we judge it as having no soul if all its energies are devoted merely to keeping itself alive and growing. We attribute soul to those entities that use some portion of their energy not only for their own sake but to make contact with other beings and care for them ... Thus we infer the existence of soul when a system uses some of its surplus energy to reach outside itself and invest it in another system, becoming in the process a stakeholder in an entity larger than itself.*

---

* Csikszentmahalyi, *Good Business*, p. 145.

84

With this thought in mind, it could be argued that the cocker spaniel has a bigger soul than the heartless lawyer who devotes all of his energies to serving himself. But the love that makes the workplace *work* transcends a spaniel's genetic predisposition to protect and provide for her young. What we need at work is not a mother's nurture, a sibling's devotion, or a spouse's affection. We need the intelligent, soul-powered love of colleagues and leaders who will spot our best self, believe it can be achieved, and work with us to pull it out.

We're not looking for a love driven by animal instinct. We're looking for a love inspired by soul. Soul is critical. The bigger the soul, the more it seeks to extend itself to invest in the highest good of another. In short, the soul's stature is measured by the yardstick of love.

Love is the metric of maturity. Got a soul? How big is it? You can tell by the amount of energy you expend believing in others and pulling the best out of them. You can tell by the amount of energy you expend seeking the growth and preservation of an ever-broadening community.

Your journey of maturity started when you began to share toys with other toddlers. It continued with your friends as you protected them in the schoolyard. It progressed when you defended a colleague's reputation at work. Perhaps you'll get married and have children. That part of the journey will give you millions of opportunities to grow your soul.

The journey of love continues in ever-expanding orbits of contribution as you seek the highest good of your community and your entire world. As Simone Weil puts it: "All the goods of this world … are finite and limited and radically incapable of satisfying the desire that perpetually burns within us for an infinite and perfect good."

SPOTTING SOMEONE'S TRUE POTENTIAL

How do you come to know and believe in someone? It typically starts with the momentary shimmer of potential you see out of the corner of your eye. This creates a bit of a gap: a sense of tension. This tension produces curiosity: a passion to connect the dots—a love of the subject that won't quit until things make sense. Mastery, in fact, is never achieved without love. As Fadiman and Frager point out in their book *Essential Sufism*:

> Whatever we wish to know well, we must love. We can't master any field of study—whether music, art, an academic field, or a profession—unless we love what we are studying. Study without love leads to a shallow, superficial understanding. Real mastery comes from love.*

And love of the subject is most crucial when it comes to knowing what's inside another human being. Here's how Viktor Frankl unpacks this concept:

---

* Fadiman and Frager, p. 113.

Love is the only way to grasp another human being in the innermost core of his personality. No one can become fully aware of the very essence of another human being unless he loves him. By his love he is enabled to see the essential traits and features in the beloved person; and even more, he sees that which is potential in him, which is not yet actualized but yet ought to be actualized.[*]

Perhaps you have noticed this dynamic in your relationship with a loved one. Your love has energized you to discover things about them that others overlook. In one sense, you've become a master on this particular "subject." And because you've extended yourself to invest in and understand this person, you are uniquely equipped to serve their highest good.

Note, however, that "the best" or "the highest good" are not things you can define on your own. They are co-discovered with the person you are investing in. We'll explore how this co-discovery occurs in the next chapter, "Love Pulls Out the Highest Good."

Spotting someone's true potential is a crucial leadership skill. As Max De Pree puts it:

The driving force in our organizations, both for-profit and not-for-profit, ought not to be goal achievement or asset management or quantifiable growth, important as

---

[*]   Frankl, pp. 111–12.

these are. Rather, our society badly needs organizations and people that move relentlessly toward realizing their potential.*

Just imagine if our workplaces were known as places of realized potential, the places people pointed to as the one area in their lives where they were growing and developing. Sadly, this is rarely the case today. And maybe that's why so many surveys point to employees not feeling developed by their leaders. We've tried every technique available to develop people to their full potential except the one that is proven to do it: love.

To generate the kind of results Dr. Dean Ornish and Dr. Mimi Silbert are achieving, we need to learn how to believe in the highest good that is possible for every person.

WHAT IS THE "HIGHEST GOOD"?

If someone said to you, "Describe for me in one word what you wish for the person you love the most," what would you say?

I would say, without batting an eye, "flourishing." I want to see my wife and children and grandchildren flourish in every single dimension of their lives: education; career; relationships; physical health; mental, emotional, and spiritual well-being; and finances. This one word encompasses a state of enjoyment and transcendence that goes far beyond survival. *Flourishing*, for me, sums up the notion of highest good.

---

* De Pree, p. 10.

Yes, I want them to live in a state of security, freedom, and belonging, but I want them to enjoy far more than that. I want them to enjoy a state of significance, fulfillment, and transcendence. Would you settle for anything less for the ones you love the most?

Love starts with a belief: the belief that there is a highest good in every person and in every situation. Without this belief, there is little to pull out of the conversation, little to serve, to care for, or to challenge.

But love doesn't stop at asking the question, "What's possible?" It goes further and asks, "What are the potentialities that lie dormant inside this person? What would flourishing look like for them?"

Sometimes I hold up a kernel of corn and ask a group, "What's in this kernel?" People usually say things like "starch," "sugar," or "the genetic blueprint of corn."

"I agree with you," I say, "and I think there's something more in here."

At this point, I uncover a ten-foot stalk of corn with two or three cobs on it. "Here's what's in this kernel," I say. "A ten-foot stalk of corn with three cobs, each with three hundred and thirty-three kernels. This single kernel has a thousand others dormant within it, and if we planted those thousand kernels, we might have a million more the following year. Plant them one more time and we would have a field of corn. Ultimately, there's a cornfield in this kernel."

I wonder what Martin Luther King's grade three teacher saw inside him. Did she see millions of people experiencing freedom?

I wonder what Bill Gates's mom Mary saw in him. Did she spot the entrepreneur and the philanthropist hidden inside her geeky twelve-year-old?

I think it would be very difficult to foresee a person's potential with that level of accuracy. I do think, however, that *love has an eye for potential*. It is always seeking to spot the better self. It looks through a small aperture to see past the person's current traits to their expansive, unfolding future.

You can learn to spot potential by paying attention to people's:

* *Talents:* A talent as a recurring knack or gift that allows a person to do something with ease. Every person has activities in which they "feel strong." Doing these things requires little energy for them and points you to their true potential. See Buckingham and Coffman's books *First, Break All the Rules* and *Now, Discover Your Strengths* to get the hang of identifying talents.

* *Interests:* Their passions and dreams will give you a window into what they're wired to do.

* *Values:* Learn to detect people's personal value systems by noticing what they make sacrifices for, what they protect at any cost, what they polish and prize, and what brightens their bulb.

* *Personality profiles:* Gain a basic knowledge of tools like Myers-Briggs Type Inventory, DISC, Social Styles, Kolbe Index, Insights, True Colors, and Strengths Deployment Inventory so you can understand what makes people tick.

* *Stories:* The skill of Appreciative Inquiry allows you to tap into a person's defining moments or an accomplishment the person is proudest of. Understanding these things gives you a window into the person's true potential.

> **Love is not** a blind belief that anybody can do anything, the notion that whatever someone puts their mind to is possible for them.
>
> **Love is** believing that there is a highest good for each person in every situation: a concrete act of service that life is requesting of them.

Because love believes in the highest good, it becomes engrossed, even obsessed, with it. It becomes passionate about, even insistent upon, actualizing it in the life and experience of the person loved. But we have to be careful here. Sometimes the highest good is very different from what we imagine.

THE MYSTERIOUS GOOD

Steve Jobs's trajectory of success was pretty remarkable. At twenty he started Apple in his parents' garage. In ten years Apple was a $2 billion company with over four thousand employees. At twenty-nine, he released his opus, the Macintosh. And then he got fired. Everything he had devoted himself to was summarily stripped from him.

Jobs was devastated, not knowing what he should do or where he should turn. He felt he had failed miserably. As he puts it:

> But something slowly began to dawn on me. I still loved what I did. The turn of events at Apple had not changed that one bit. I had been rejected, but I was still in love. And so I decided to start over.

> I didn't see it then, but it turned out that getting fired from Apple was the best thing that could have ever happened to me. The heaviness of being successful was replaced by the lightness of being a beginner again, less sure about everything. It freed me to enter one of the most creative periods of my life.

> During the next five years, I started a company named NeXT, another company named Pixar, and fell in love

with an amazing woman who would become my wife. Pixar went on to create the world's first computer animated feature film, *Toy Story*, and is now the most successful animation studio in the world. In a remarkable turn of events, Apple bought NeXT, I returned to Apple, and the technology we developed at NeXT is at the heart of Apple's current renaissance. And Laurene and I have a wonderful family together.

I'm pretty sure none of this would have happened if I hadn't been fired from Apple.*

In all our talk about flourishing, actualizing potentialities, and meeting core emotional needs, let's not lose sight of a very simple reality: Human beings are a mystery. A little humility will not hurt us here. Let's work with people to divine the highest good for them. Let's grasp the essence of people's talents and passions and try our best to understand the destination to which those things might point. But let's also understand that an event as catastrophic as being fired may be the highest good for someone, even (gulp) for us, in the long run.

And when you've tried your best and still can't spot the social reformer or the philanthropist hidden inside someone, how do you facilitate the emergence of their potential? A short, simple set of markers can help you. By helping people meet their felt needs of fit, clarity, support, value, and inspiration, you build

---

* Jobs, "You've Got to Find What You Love."

the conditions in which they can actualize their potential. Whenever you help them experience these felt needs, you are pulling the cornfield out of the kernel.

What's in these five feelings that enables a person to actualize her potentialities? The removal of interference that optimizes performance:

$$P = \frac{T + E + K}{I}$$

Fit: The emotions of validity, inclusion, belonging, and hope remove the interference associated with the fear of being rejected.

Clarity: The emotions of confidence and certainty remove the interference associated with the insecurity of confusion.

Support: The emotions of provision, protection, equipping, flow, and ease remove the interference associated with distraction.

Value: The emotions of respect, worth, significance, self-esteem, dignity, and honor remove the interference associated with lack of confidence.

Inspiration: The emotions of fulfillment, growth, achievement, self-actualization, transcendence, and meaning remove the interference associated with malaise and lack of purpose.

Love has an eye for potential. Given the talent shortage (not people shortage) that organizations are facing today, we had better get some of that love into our eyes pretty fast. Talented people have a keen sense for whether you recognize their talent. They will be attracted to or driven from cultures where belief is not demonstrated.

And how do you demonstrate that you believe the best? You work with people to pull out their highest good. This is exactly where we will focus our attention next.

7 | LOVE PULLS OUT THE HIGHEST GOOD

Love is the fine amalgam of courage and selflessness that mature human beings use to release creative energy out of their life tensions.

Every July I return to Manitoulin Island in Lake Huron to the cottage where I spent the summers of my youth. It's not all fun and games up north. A few years ago we had to replace the wiring between two of the cottages. Because the new wire was going to be buried, the job entailed running a thick electrical wire through a plastic hose that would protect the wire underground.

PUSH OR PULL?

How to get 140 feet of wire through 140 feet of plastic hose: That was the challenge. Mike, the hardware store guy, had offered some advice, but it seemed farfetched and much too time-consuming. My brother, Tim, and I decided to try what we thought would be a faster and easier method.

First, we uncoiled the wire and stretched it out in a straight line along the beach. Then we tried pushing the wire through the hose. What we thought would be a relatively simple process proved futile. Although the wire was stiff, the friction proved to be too much, getting things to the point where we could no longer push the wire at all.

What to do next? We thought of taking the wire and the hose and hanging them over the edge of nearby East Bluff. Maybe gravity would overcome the friction and the wire would slowly fall through the hose. But it would take a lot of work to roll up the wire and the hose, drive it up to the bluff, unroll it over the edge, slide the wire through the hose (which we weren't sure would work), roll the hose back up, and drive it back to the lake.

Mike the hardware guy's method was beginning to look more and more attractive, despite the fact that it would require significant upfront work.

Tim took a little piece of a plastic bag and tied a roll of fishing line to it. I stuck the piece of plastic bag into one end of the hose and Tim went to the other end and stuck a small vacuum cleaner over the end. He turned on the vacuum cleaner and before we knew it, the suction had pulled the fishing line through the hose and to his end.

We then used the fishing line to pull a sturdy string through the hose. Once the string was through, we attached it to the electric wire. We all watched with amazement as I was able to walk along the beach, pulling the thick wire through the hose quickly and easily.

The lesson was embarrassingly clear to us: When it comes to getting something flexible through a conduit, pulling works a lot better than pushing. Pulling reduces unnecessary friction and enables you to get something through in a shorter time and with less stress.

We had defaulted to a push-first approach because we thought it would take too long to pull. We ended up wasting all the time we spent pushing, in the end being forced to invest the time on the pull approach anyway.

When you need to get your point across to somebody, do you push or pull? There is an inherent problem with push: *People will tolerate your conclusions and act on their own conclusions.* Your intellect, your passion, or your tenacity can wear someone down to the point that they will nod their head and agree with you. But when you walk away, they will take action on their own conclusions, not yours.

If your default behavior is to push, you have lots of company. In our studies over the last sixteen years, we have discovered that about 60 percent of the population resorts to push when they need to be understood.

TEN REASONS YOU PUSH THOSE YOU LOVE

1. You see what they can become, and they just can't see it ("If I just push a little more, I know they'll get it.")

2. You **want so badly** for them to experience this.

3. You **feel responsible** for their well-being.

4. They'll **pay more attention** to you if they see you're passionate about this.

5. Because if you pull, they may mistakenly assume you are **endorsing their point of view.**

6. There just isn't enough time to pull. We need to get this happening.

7. You are in a position of **authority**. It is your right to push. Their job is to understand.

8. If their way gets adopted, it **won't be best** for them, others, or you.

9. No one has ever **taught** you how to pull.

10. It's what was **modeled** to you (those who loved you pushed you).

THE CONNECTION-MAKING MACHINE

You may remember the story of Archimedes the mathematician who was charged by a ruler to determine whether the crown that had been made for him was pure gold or contained silver, a substance of inferior value.

Archimedes wrestled long and hard with the problem and had despaired of finding a solution when one evening, at the end of a hard day of calculus, he sank into a hot tub and noticed the water level rise at the side of the bath.

Something fired in his brain and he instantly knew the answer to his dilemma: It all had to do with volume displacement. He jumped out of the bath buck naked and ran through the streets of the city crying, "Eureka! Eureka!"

In his book *Quiet Leadership*, David Rock explains that the human brain is a connection-making machine. You've been mulling a problem over and over in your mind. In the middle of the night, you sit bolt upright in your bed as the synapses of your brain make a new connection, releasing a sudden surge of energy. (Maybe not enough to send you running through the streets yelling "Eureka!" but energy nonetheless.)

This feature of the brain is critical for us to understand as managers and leaders. In the era of the knowledge worker, one of our primary accountabilities is to cultivate the decision-making velocity of our employees. The problem is, when employees come to us with a problem, our first instinct is to solve it for them. But by doling out the information, we unwittingly rob them of the surge of energy that comes from the discovery experience.

Why is this important? Because people need energy to execute on their ideas. Remember, people will take action on their own conclusions, not yours. Why? Because their conclusions are infused with a surge of energy. So use a Pull approach with your employees by asking the powerful questions that spark a discovery. That way employees will come to their own conclusions and have the fuel onboard for follow-through. You can use this principle in many situations: coaching, giving feedback, and brainstorming, to name a few. Here's an example of how you can use it to help an employee with goal-setting.

PULL OUT A SMART GOAL

I am a proponent of SMART goals. I help leaders co-create goals that are Specific, Meaningful, Agreed-upon, Realistic, and Time-bound.

I've helped many leaders boost their effectiveness by taking a different approach with the "S" part of SMART—ensuring that the goal is *specific*.

Most often, leaders focus their energy on the quantitative parts of specificity, ignoring the qualitative parts: the evocative parts that release the passion and impetus necessary for the goal's achievement.

For example, an employee says to me, "I want to get better at managing my time."

Is that a SMART goal? No. So I start pulling: "Can you give me a picture of what your time-management skills look like right now?"

"Oh sure. Well, just yesterday I missed an important phone meeting because my planner wasn't synched up properly. I don't get to projects until the last minute and end up working late into the evening. I have to bother my co-workers late at night for stuff. My desk is a disaster and it makes my whole mind feel cluttered."

"It sounds like this is consuming a lot of mental energy for you."

"You bet it is."

"Okay. So if ten is your life as a well-oiled time-management machine and zero is your life in absolute chaos, where are you right now?"

"Oh I'm a four. Definitely a four."

"You're a four. And where do you want to be?"

"Well I'd love to be a ten."

"And is that realistic for you?"

"Probably not."

"What is realistic for you?"

"A seven."

"Okay. So you want to move from a four to a seven. In what time period? By next week? Three years from now?"

"I'd say if I could move from a four to a seven in three months, that would be a very good thing."

"And is that realistic?"

"Yes, with some coaching, some practice, and some accountability, I believe it is."

"Very well. Can you give me a picture of what a seven will look like in your world?"

"Sure, my desk would be clean. My whole office would be organized. I would be on time for meetings. I'd be finishing projects a few days in advance rather than one or two days late. I'd be working fewer evenings. Instead I'd be helping coach my little girl's soccer team."

"Several of those things are fairly measurable. Could you tell me whether you're at a seven or not in three months?"

"I could and my co-workers could, too. I believe the goal is measurable."

"Perfect. Okay, so I get a picture of what your seven looks like. What will the pay-off be for you if you can achieve your seven within the next ninety days?"

"My thinking will be clearer. My decision making will be more confident. I'll have more energy. I'll have more respect here at work and fewer fights at home."

"The implications of this are big. So this is a meaningful goal for you."

"It's huge for me."

"So how can I help you achieve this?"

And the conversation moves forward from there.

At this point, we not only have a goal that is Specific, Meaningful, Agreed-upon, Realistic, and Time-bound, we have a clear mental picture of what it will look like and feel like to achieve that goal. This is a critical because it releases the energy required for follow-through.

PULL CAN TAKE STUFF OFF YOUR PLATE

Eric, a marketing VP of a highly successful company, recently told us about his shift from push to pull. A manager who reports to him had been facing significant challenges at home. Eric's conversations with her left him feeling frustrated and her feeling unfulfilled. He had focused his efforts on taking work off the manager's plate so she could deal with the pressures at home.

When Eric went through our Pull Conversation training, he learned how to put on the manager's eyes and understand the implications of her situation. This enabled him to detect her feelings, which in turn told him what she needed and, just as importantly, what she didn't need in this situation. Eric made a surprising discovery when he pulled: that giving this manager more challenges at work left her with more energy to deal with her challenges at home.

Eric's intent was to support this manager, but it hadn't come across as felt support at all. Shifting from push to pull allowed Eric to frame up a strategy that released three valuable resources: focus to the manager, time to him, and productivity to the organization.

PULL DRAWS OUT THE BEST

A Pull approach makes the smartest decisions become apparent, but as Brenda Ueland conveys in the following story, they can also draw out some of the finest behaviors.

Recently I saw a man I had not seen for twenty years. He was an unusually forceful man and had made a great deal of money. But he had lost his ability to listen. He talked rapidly and told wonderful stories and it was just fascinating to hear them. But when I spoke—restlessness: "Just hand me that, will you? . . . Where is my pipe?"

I said to myself: "He has been under a driving pressure for years. His family has grown to resist his talk. But now, by listening, I will pull it all out of him. He must talk freely and on and on. When he has been really listened to enough, he will grow tranquil. He will begin to want to hear me."

And he did, after a few days. He began asking me questions. And presently I was saying gently: "You see, it has become hard for you to listen."

He stopped dead and stared at me. And it was because I had listened with such complete, absorbed, uncritical sympathy, without one flaw of boredom or impatience, that he now believed and trusted me, although he did not know this.

"Now talk," he said. "Tell me more about that. Tell me all about that."*

Ueland then had an opportunity to offer some thoughtful advice to her friend that would help him fulfill his true potential.

As Dr. John Gottman, one of America's relationship experts, says, "Human nature dictates that it is virtually impossible to accept advice from someone unless you feel that person understands you. People can only change if they feel that they are basically liked and accepted as they are."**

As Ueland puts it:

---

* Ueland, *Strength to Your Sword Arm.*
** Gottman and Silver, p. 149.

Unless you listen, people are wizened in your presence; they become about a third of themselves. Unless you listen, you can't know anybody. Oh. You will know facts and what is in the newspapers and all of history, perhaps, but you will not know one single person. You know, I have come to think listening is love, that's what it really is.*

The poet William Butler Yeats writes, "We can make our minds so like still water that beings gather about us, that they may see their own images, and so live for a moment with a clearer, perhaps even a fiercer life because of our quiet."

When you push, people tend to push back. When you pull, they tend to open up. This dynamic was dubbed the law of psychological reciprocity by author Robert K. Greenleaf. We tend to trust those who trust us, respect those who respect us, and understand those who understand us. As my friend Loretta's story illustrates, this law has efficacy in even the most intractable of situations.

CHANGING THE UNCHANGEABLE

Everyone in Loretta's department avoided Mryna. She was fifty years old and was heading toward retirement. She had worked in the company forever and was an indispensable support person, handling all of the department's bookings with clients. Indeed, externally, she was very courteous. Her customers liked deal-

---

*   Ueland, *Strength to Your Sword Arm.*

ing with her on the phone. Internally, however, she was short-tempered, crude, and belligerent. Getting your work needs met through her was messy, time-consuming, and frustrating.

Loretta was just as horrified by Myrna as everyone else but had the unenviable position of being one of several people Myrna supported. Loretta could see that Myrna was a needy person but she had a tiny bit of belief that Myrna had potential inside her that could be pulled out. So she decided to try paying attention to her for ten minutes every day. Both of them were early birds, so she thought a bit of conversation first thing in the day would make the difference. It would be easy.

It wasn't easy, but it did make a difference.

At first Loretta regretted her decision. In her maiden voyage of pulling out Myrna's reality, as the ten minutes stretched to half an hour, she didn't know how to extricate herself. The second day was no better. By the third, she was ready to pull out her hair. But on that third day, Myrna seemed a little more human, and Loretta managed to get out of her office after twenty minutes.

And so it went. Every day, Loretta believed in Myrna and invested the psychological capital of pulling out her true potential. Though she often cringed at Myrna's comments, she put aside her reactions, determined to keep listening.

Myrna was as grouchy as ever with everyone else but began to care about Loretta's work and delivered it on time, and, miraculously, free of mistakes. Loretta began to see that Myrna was more capable than she had imagined. Eventually the short visits became much more pleasant.

Loretta was the lucky recipient of several revelations about Myrna: that Myrna acted the way she did because of her unmet needs; that she did have competencies; and that she could be funny and even creative at times.

When you believe in someone's potential, it's only natural to try to pull that potential from the inside out. Perhaps others cannot see the potential. They see the Myrnas for what they are rather than for what they can be. Life's mad pace causes many of us to ignore certain people. Respect compels leaders like Loretta to do otherwise. They think, "Maybe there is potential here that I missed on my first flyby," and go back for another look.

Interestingly enough, having another look is what respect is all about. It comes from the Latin word *respecere*, which means, *to look again*. In his book *Dialogue: The Art of Thinking Together*, Bill Isaacs says that respect "involves a sense of honoring or defer-ring to someone. Where once we saw one aspect of a person, we look again and realize how much of them we had missed."

This respectful type of Pull Conversation is the operating sys-tem of successful organizations. Like any operating system, it drives all the applications: sales, coaching, customer service, strategy, and marketing. They all run off Pull Conversation. When we pull out someone's highest good, we meet their most important needs, which releases energy inside them: energy that can unlock the discretionary effort of a seemingly cantankerous employee like Myrna.

> **Love is not** seeing a glimpse of someone's true potential and pushing it from the outside in.
>
> **Love is** seeing a glimpse of someone's true potential and pulling it from the inside out.

THE HIGHEST GOOD IS PULLED OUT, NOT PUSHED IN

Why pull? Because you don't fully see the highest good and neither does the other person. It has to be teased out and revealed, manifested by life.

A story told about Alfred Hitchcock illustrates this point:

> We were working on a problem with a scene. There were a lot of things to consider—lighting, staging, pacing, and the like. We were up very late struggling to find the right way to do it. Finally, when we seemed close to the solution, Hitchcock came in and started telling jokes, silly, junior high-type stuff, and got us all lost again. Later, I asked him why, when we were so close to solving the problem, did he choose that moment to get us off track by joking around? He paused, and then said something I'll never forget. He said, "You were pushing. It never comes from pushing."[*]

---

[*] Muller, p. 190.

Push seems to be part of the human condition. The path of those seeking to help others actualize their potentialities has been fraught with blunders. You don't have to look any farther than religion to witness this: Belief starts out pure and turns into a manipulative push in the blink of an eye.

So what should you do when you see potential—something you believe a person can become—but they just can't see it yet? You don't always have the luxury of waiting for months or years for the potentiality to blossom. Here's where you use Pull Conversation to find a fivefold highest good that meets the needs of the employee, the team, the organization, the customer, and you.

As I said above, about two-thirds of the population push when they want someone to change or they need to get their point across. Push does work well for debate (which literally means *to beat down your opponent*) and for discussion (which means *to shake apart*). But if your goal is dialogue, push drives at cross purposes, actually blocking the relational conduit. People become defensive and start to shut down.

Dialogue literally means *reality flowing through*. Pull Conversation is an approach that is perfectly suited to draw reality through the conduit of a relationship.

The mindset of Pull is all about drawing the biggest truth, the biggest reality, out of any situation. You have a reality (your truth) and the other person has a reality (their truth). You think you are right. They think they are right. Usually, there's a bigger right, a bigger truth, a bigger reality that lies latent between the two of you.

A Pull Conversation is based on the simple premise that when people feel understood by you, they are more willing to understand you. By pulling first, you can get your point across to people in about half the time it would take by pushing. (The concept of Pull is fully unpacked in my book *Juice: The Power of Conversation*.)

So a Pull Conversation starts with you pulling out the other person's reality. Then you pull them into your reality, using invitational language. Once you clearly understand each other's realities, you uncover the common ground by asking, "What is it we both want here?"

Common ground is the fertile soil from which the bigger reality or the highest good emerges. You don't pull it out by force, you gently draw it out, tease it out. In the words of Peter Senge, in his book *Presence*, the highest good wants to manifest itself—you simply let it come.

LEARN TO LOVE PROBLEMS

One of the first rules of relationships is that in any relationship you will encounter differences. Men communicate for independence; women for intimacy. South Americans have a different sense of timeliness than North Americans do. Operations people tend to value processes differently from salespeople. Millennials and boomers appreciate technology differently. Introverts and extroverts view a company party very differently.

All these differences tend to create a sense of tension. Although for most of us tension is spelled p-r-o-b-l-e-m, there's something hidden within it that is truly powerful. Residing within tension is the resource we need to get work done: energy. And although you don't get to decide whether energy will get released from the tension, you do get to decide whether it will be intelligent energy or destructive energy.

Love lives in the tension between your needs and another's needs. Your challenge is to learn how to love by pulling out the highest good from your tension-filled situations.

You deal with business tensions every day at work. You'll recognize most of these:

  *Do what's right for the environment *and* maximize profits.

  * Do what's good for the short-term *and* the long-term.

  * Provide a differentiated, tailor-made customer experience *and* reduce costs.

  * Use technology to drive efficiency *and* help employees feel a sense of human connection.

Great leaders stand right in the middle of the tension, and, using the power of Pull, harmonize conflicting priorities. In so doing, they release a powerful energy that drives sustainable results. As Gary Semplonius, a Bell Canada VP, once said in a speech to a group of high-potential directors that I was training, "If you want to be a great leader, there's one thing you need to do more than anything else: learn to love problems."

In relationships, love lives right in the middle of the tension: right in the middle of your needs and the other's needs. If you are frequently repressing your needs to meet another's needs, that is not love. If you are frequently getting your needs met at the expense of another's, that is not love either. The following model reveals how love exists in the tension between your needs and others.

Love Lives in the Tension

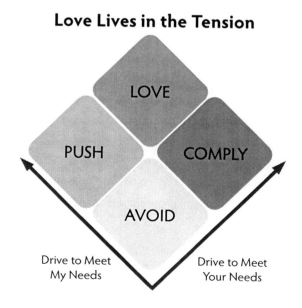

117

When my drive to meet your needs is high but the drive to meet my needs is low, I will comply. I end up invalidating my own needs while ensuring that yours get met. You are temporarily energized but may feel a bit guilty about getting your needs met at my expense. What is required here? More courage on my part.

When my drive to meet my needs is high and my drive to meet yours is low, I push and invalidate your needs in order to get mine met. This temporarily resolves the tension, but although I am energized, you walk away depleted. What is required here? More selflessness on my part.

When I suppress my needs and ignore yours, I withdraw and we are both depleted. What is required here? *More courage and more selflessness.*

Love lives in the tension between your needs and mine. It's in this tension that we pull, honoring both of our needs and drawing out a solution that achieves the highest good for all concerned. Love is the fine amalgam of courage and selflessness that mature human beings use to release the creative energy out of their life tensions.

It's the drive to get your own needs met combined with the drive to ensure that your employee's needs get met that releases energy.

Love extends grace to another's inadequacies *and* calls out their bad behavior. Love accommodates weaknesses *and* demands growth. It is in the harmonizing of our needs with another's that both of us grow and mature. It's then that the highest good emerges for both of us.

As Erich Fromm says in *The Art of Loving*, this kind of conversation places significant demands on us.

> Love is possible only if two persons communicate with each other from the center of their existence ... love, experienced thus, is a constant challenge; it is not a resting place, but a moving, growing, working together ... they are one with each other by being one with themselves, rather than by fleeing from themselves.*

Here's the issue: When you stand right in the middle of the tension, you feel an intense pressure that causes you to buckle toward push behavior or comply behavior. How many leaders, bending to that pressure, have jumped to a decision only to discover later that an elegant solution would have presented itself if only they had waited?

It is difficult, isn't it? Everything within you just wants to resolve the tension so you can make the pressure go away. Standing right in the middle of your relational or business tension will stress and tear your muscles. It will also make you a stronger, fitter leader.

---

* Fromm, p. 96.

One of the great paradoxes of leadership is that the more power and authority you have in an organization, the harder it is to connect with reality. You become insulated from it. As Michael Beer says in his work on what he calls "high commitment high performance" organizations, leaders need to create an environment where truth can speak to power.

Pull Conversation is the skill that allows leaders to do exactly that: create a place of safety in which front-line reality can emerge and catalyze with big-picture reality to produce a rich mixture that serves employees and customers. When you pull well, something powerful is unlocked: the energy to serve. Let's take a look at that next.

8 | LOVE SERVES PEOPLE'S SUCCESS

Love is creating the conditions
for your employees' success
and serving them in ways that
put them in a state of flow.

Shelly started to choke up when she told me what her boss had done for her. She had been stuck in a no-win situation. She was managing a challenging nursing unit with too few resources and was feeling drained by too many demands. She was losing too much emotional energy as she tried to deal with a chronic bullying issue.

Shelly told me, "My boss Kate came to me and said, 'I'm carrying your pager for the next six weeks while you get things straightened out. I'll let you know what you need to respond to and I'll take care of the rest.' What kind of a boss does something like that?"

I know a bit about the kind of boss who does something like that. I've witnessed Kate in action several times. She is a living example of the core message of the book *The Power of Servant Leadership* by Robert K. Greenleaf. For Kate, leading is not about the service she can render as a leader; it's about the leadership she can exercise as a servant.

Something happens when you believe in your employees: You start inquiring, asking, and pulling out the ways you can offer felt support. What happens next is beautifully predictable: Believing and pulling find their outlet in serving. You do whatever you can to create that sense of felt support. And the servant leader's purpose in serving is simple: to make the employee successful.

And as the following story illustrates, this often happens so seamlessly that the employee doesn't realize until long after just how instrumental the leader really was.

Robert Greenleaf came upon the notion of servant leadership after he read Hermann Hesse's novel *Journey to the East*. In the novel a group of sojourners is trekking through time and space in search of the spiritual order The League. They are accompanied by a servant, Leo, who selflessly attends to their physical needs by performing menial chores and who sustains their emotional needs by lifting their spirits through his songs.

At one point in the journey, Leo disappears and the group falls apart. Without his acts of service and sustaining spirit, the group is unable to cohere. The journey is abandoned. In the years that follow, the narrator of the story stumbles through life until one day he finds a piece of information that enables him to re-establish connection with Leo. He is taken into The League and discovers that Leo, the man he had known as a servant, was the head of the order.

After reading this story, Greenleaf concluded that its central meaning was that the great leader is first a servant, and that this simple fact is central to his or her greatness. True leadership emerges from those whose primary motivation is a deep desire to help others.*

Leaders like Kate are "Leos." It's easy to spot them. When

---

* Greenleaf, p. 4.

you are in their presence, you experience something startling: a sense of ease. Because their primary motivation is to serve, they make it easy for employees to showcase their talents. They remove unnecessary friction by renovating faulty systems. They advocate for their employees to minimize human wear-and-tear. This leaves employees feeling, "It's easy to work here."

Servant leadership is not the behavior of someone who is bored and doesn't know what else to do with her time. Nor is it about being nice (*nice* once meant *ignorant* or *unknowing*). The servant leader is not someone who lacks strength of character or is confused about her identity.

The servant leader is someone who has successfully turned the corner from "I'm an individual contributor" to "I contribute through others."

The servant leader gets her sense of identity from making others successful. She is ruthless in ferreting out every form of interference that sabotages an employee's performance. Her laser-beam focus on making sure her employees' core emotional needs are met helps them offer their best at work every day. She glows with excitement when she is reaching that magical point of intersection between an employee's success and the success of the organization. In fact, she will not rest until she reaches this point.

Are you a servant leader? Does your serving do what it's intended to do? To find out, take Greenleaf's simple test.

SERVANT LEADER TEST

Do those served grow as persons?

Do they, while being served, become healthier, wider, freer and more autonomous?

Are they more likely themselves to become servants because of your serving?

What is the effect on the least privileged of society; will they benefit, or at least not be further deprived?*

Imagine your employees reading the above four points and saying, "Oh yes! That is definitely my experience of having worked with so-and-so." If that's how they sum up the impact of your service, chances are you've grown as a leader. You've morphed from performance management to success management.

Mac Carter of Turning Points has done some fine work drawing a distinction between performance management and success management. In many organizations, performance management is experienced as a tool that is used to get employees to do more work faster and better. The manager using this tool is often focused on what's wrong: "What are the gaps and how do I close them?" The approach feels outside in. Feedback and

---

* Greenleaf, p. 4.

coaching are often seen as punitive measures. The best arrangement that performance management can produce is a contractual agreement.

But "success management," as Carter describes it, "is grounded in the basic assumption that the essence of a manager's job ... is to create conditions that optimize both the performance and growth of the people who report to them."*

Farm Credit Canada is an organization that serves Canada's agricultural sector. One of Canada's best organizations to work for, FCC has created a culture in which people act as committed partners, striving for one another's success.

They've captured the heart of success management: taking a stand for their people's success as committed partners and enabling them to flourish and achieve their true potential. In success management, the manager is focused on creating the conditions for success: leveraging strengths, removing interference, and meeting core emotional needs. The approach is inside-out, and feedback and coaching are viewed as pivotal. Success management produces an arrangement where employees think and act like business owners.

Can you find out what someone needs to feel successful? Absolutely. You ask them certain questions.

---

* http://www.turningpoints.com/resources/SuccessMgt.pdf

* "What do you need to feel successful in the next six months?"

* "What do you need to feel successful throughout the project?"

* "What do you need to feel successful in the midst of this merger?"

CREATE A STATE OF FLOW

One of the best ways to serve someone's success is to create the conditions in which they can experience a state of flow. *Flow* is a term coined by Mihaly Csikszentmihalyi, a psychology professor at the University of Chicago. In the mid-seventies, he and a team of researchers began what ultimately became a multiyear, quarter-million-dollar volunteer study that penetrated the black box of optimal human experience.

To measure the quality of experience that people report at various moments in their lives, Csikszentmihalyi and his team had volunteers carry a programmable signaling device (watch, PDA, etc.) and a journal. The device went off at random eight to ten times a day. When this happened, the volunteer was to write down the circumstances they were in, what they were thinking and feeling, the challenges they were engaged with, and the level of skill they were utilizing. To add further context and depth to these data, the researchers conducted more than eight thousand interviews with their volunteers.

Perhaps you can imagine just how stunning these data were and how groundbreaking the results of this study would prove to be. In short, the researchers discovered the conditions that put a human being into a state of flow. Csikszentmihalyi defines a flow state is one in which a person feels:

> ... carried away by an outside force ... moved effortlessly with a current of energy ... drawn into the complexity of the task ... forgets about himself ... loses touch with the rest of the world ... and loses all track of time.*

You've experienced this. You were completely immersed in what you are doing, then something jarred you, you looked at your watch, and you simply could not fathom where the time had gone. At that point you almost had to tear yourself away from the activity you were absorbed in. This is typical of the flow state. But how do you re-create it?

Csikszentmihalyi details several conditions required to trigger this state of flow. I've condensed his list to the five conditions that I've found to be most significant.

1. **A healthy challenge:** The challenge is just beyond your capability.

2. **A clear goal:** You have a clear mental picture of what success looks like.

---

* Csikszentmihalyi, *Good Business*, pp. 39–41.

3. **Minimal distractions:** You can focus intensely without interference.

4. **Immediate feedback:** You know specifically what you need to do to improve.

5. **A meaningful task:** You sense you're a part of something greater.

We now see a confluence of several streams of thought. The servant leader uses love's actions and the Five Drivers to remove interference and create the flow conditions for the employee's success. Wherever you experience love at work you'll see a leader who:

1. **Believes the best** and finds the **fit** between your capabilities and the challenge of the task.

2. Works with you to **pull out** the highest good: a **clear** mental picture of what success looks like.

3. **Serves your success** with the types of **support** that will remove distractions.

4. **Cares for your worth** and **values** you by recognizing your successes and letting you know exactly what you can do to improve.

5. **Challenges you to stretch, inspiring** you with the meaning of your work.

Does your leader do these things for you, enabling you to enter into a state of flow? Are you doing these things for your employees? Here's where the Five Drivers can help you focus your efforts as a leader. Every time you invest psychological capital in creating fit, clarity, support, value, and inspiration, you create the conditions for flow.

Love is not being a doormat for your employees, enabling unproductive behaviors or doing their work for them.

Love is creating the conditions for your employees' success and serving them in ways that put them in a state of flow.

ARISTOTLE'S PICTURE

Around 333 B.C. Aristotle said that the soul never thinks without a picture. Many notable sports psychologists have locked onto this ancient concept. They believe you can perform only what you have pictured. Their focus with elite athletes is to create a clear mental picture of the perfect hurdle, the perfect quad, the perfect dive. By the time the diver's body slices into the water, he is simply executing what he has already visualized in his mind thousands of times.

If people can perform only what they have pictured, what are the implications of this for you as a leader? They are significant.

For instance, did you just communicate your wishes to an employee? If you didn't leave her with a clear mental picture of what you want to occur, then you haven't truly communicated.

You may object, "But I told her!" However, if Aristotle is right, no picture = no performance.

Do you have a vision statement on your wall? Does it create a compelling picture of the future that releases energy inside your employees? No picture = no performance.

Did you just spend time giving an employee recognition for his performance? Was he left with a clear picture of how his behavior contributed to the organization's success? No picture = no reproducible performance.

Did you just spend time in a goal-setting session with an employee? If she is not left with a clear mental picture of what success will look and feel like, her chances of achieving the goal are slim. No picture = no performance.

There is one area in particular where your ability to help employees see a clear mental picture will serve their success significantly. Let's take a look at that area now.

THE BROADCAST OF INTENTION

A year ago I read a book called *The Dream Manager*. It's a parable by Matthew Kelley about Admiral Janitorial Services, a 407-employee organization struggling with a 400 percent annual turnover rate that was costing the company $170,000 a month.

As the company began to ask employees why people were leaving Admiral, they ultimately discovered a radical solution to their dilemma: hire a dream manager to help employees fulfill their dreams. The dream manager's coaching enabled employees to buy their first home, get their high school diploma, or do other things that had previously seemed impossible.

The impact on engagement and turnover was remarkable, creating a financial return that easily covered the dream manager's salary.

The book concludes by encouraging the reader to create a Dream Book, writing down as many dreams as possible.

I guess I don't really stack up in the dream department. I came up with only a third of the recommended number of one hundred. But what has happened over the past year has really caught my attention.

One of my dreams was to cross the finish line of a full marathon with my family there to share the moment with me. That happened only two months after I wrote the dream in my Dream Book (even though at that point I had run nothing longer than a ten-kilometer race).

Another dream was to help a third world family launch their own business and become self-sufficient. Over the next twelve months, my business partner, Alex Somos, and I helped launch twenty-five such businesses.

I have been amazed to actualize other dreams, as well. Why am I amazed? Because I always thought you had to have goals to accomplish something tangible. How could dreams cut it?

I've learned something valuable: that there are three things you can do to make your dreams come true.

1. See a clear mental picture of what you dream to do.

2. Write your intention down in dream form.

3. Return to it again and again to visualize it accomplished.

When you do these things, your whole world goes to work to align the circumstances that will bring your dream to pass. Srikumar Rao, professor of marketing at Columbia Business School and a contributing editor of *Forbes*, puts it this way:

> Thinking about your intention many, many times—is, in a sense, a broadcast of intention. When you broadcast such an intention, there's very little else you have to do. The broadcast of intention goes out and makes it happen.

Your role is to remain keenly aware, patiently expectant, and open to all possibilities.*

Here's how you can serve people's success. You can be a dream manager and use Pull Conversation to help them see a clear mental image of their dream. You can then work with them to identify the pragmatic steps they can take to facilitate the fulfillment of their dream.

Do you want to leave a powerful Leo-like legacy? Here's what you can do:

* Become a servant leader who manages peoples' success rather than just their performance.

* Create the conditions that allow people to get into the flow state.

* Enable employees to fulfill their dreams by helping them create a clear mental picture of their success and broadcast it into reality.

This type of servant leadership sends an unmistakable message to your workforce: that you are a leader who cares about people. Let's move forward to the powerful concept of care now.

---

* Senge et al., *Presence*, pp. 134-35.

9 | LOVE CARES FOR PEOPLE'S WORTH

Why does care elicit such a
visceral response?
Simple: It touches something vital
inside us—our sense of worth.

The year was 1930. It was the Great Depression. Jobs were nowhere to be found. In a bold attempt to create three hundred jobs for those who had been put out of work, W.K. Kellogg redesigned his cereal plant production schedule from three eight-hour shifts to four six-hour shifts. The rest of the workers took a slight pay cut.

Elisabeth Goodridge explains what happened next.

> The company found that the shorter workday influenced employees to work harder and more efficiently. The results included drastic reductions in overhead costs, labor costs, and the number of work-related accidents. Unit cost of production "is so lowered we can afford to pay as much for six hours as we formerly paid for eight," Kellogg boasted in a newspaper in 1935.

Improvement was even more dramatic outside the factory, in the town of Battle Creek. "For the first time they had real leisure," writes Benjamin Kline Hunnicutt, professor of leisure arts at the University of Iowa, in his book *Kellogg's Six-Hour Day* (Temple University Press, 1996). Parents spent more time with their children, in the neighborhood, and at libraries. Women gardened, canned, sewed, and made ice cream; men played baseball and softball, hunted, and farmed.*

When you see someone expending the effort of redesigning a

---

* Goodridge, "Six-hour Shifts Satisfied Kellogg's Appetite for Productivity."

plant-wide production schedule, stick-handling through the bad news of a pay-cut, hiring and training three hundred new people, and then paying the whole plant eight hours' wages for six hours' of work, there's a good chance you're seeing love at work.

And how did the employees respond to such a leader?

They offered an extra 33 percent discretionary effort: eight hours of productivity in six hours of work.

And what are the broader community implications?

It began to flourish. There was more time to spend with children, in the libraries, and in social interaction.

Are you as a leader responsible for ensuring that employees have energy left over at the end of the day: energy for their spouse, their kids, their community? Some leaders believe so. They see themselves as cultural architects, building the conditions in which people can flourish on the job and at home.

However, leaders can do this only if they care. Unfortunately, many employees are left with the distinct impression that hard assets are more important to their leaders than people are.

"I JUST DO WHAT I'M TOLD"

The ultimate travesty is a workplace filled with employees who don't care. They don't care about the customer. They don't care about quality. They don't care about results. I will never forget an interview I had with Jason, an employee at a distribution center who used to be a star performer and now was someone who no longer cared.

"I loved finding the best ways to do things," he told me. "I'd think about my job in the evenings and even wake up in the middle of the night with ideas on how to improve our processes. When my shift was over and everybody else was heading home, I would spend five to ten minutes and leave notes on top of the pallets so the next shift would know exactly what had to happen with the products. They told me it not only added to their productivity, it multiplied it."

"So what happened to change all that?" I asked.

"I was moving some pallets when my forklift nudged a rack piled with bags of dog food. The rack wasn't properly secured, and hundreds of pounds of the stuff came tumbling down. It just missed me.

"I was pretty shaken up, but thankful to be alive. Then I heard my manager and the VP come running out into the plant. Do you want to know the first words that came out of their mouths?"

"I imagine they asked you, 'Are you all right?' "

"Yeah, I wish. They got right in my face and said, 'How much dog food just got wasted here?' "

I could see on Jason's face the profound sense of disrespect he had felt.

"When I finally realized that they didn't care about me, that's the day that everything changed for me. It used to be that I'd come in and work overtime just to help my manager out. Now when they ask me to work overtime, I tell them I've got other things to do. And I don't look for better ways to do things anymore. I just do what I'm told."

There it is, the ultimate indictment against leadership: "I just do what I'm told." When people feel you care, they offer you their best stuff. When they feel you don't care, they find a thousand overt or covert ways to give you the bare minimum.

So what is care and what does it produce inside an employee?

"I'LL DO ANYTHING FOR THAT GUY!"

I was asked to design a training program for the law enforcement leaders who engage with Ontario Police College. In preparation for this task, I interviewed officers to gain a clear picture of what star performance looks like in the ranks of staff sergeants, detectives, and inspectors.

William told me, "When I walk into my staff sergeant's office, he lays down his pen, takes off his reading glasses, shuts off his computer monitor, looks me right in the eye, and says, 'So, William, what would you like to talk about?'"

And then William said something that startled me: "I'll do anything for that guy."

"That's quite something to say about someone who's just listening to you," I said.

"No. You don't get it. I feel respected by him—like he really cares about what's going on in my world."

Smart leaders prove their care with specific, observable behaviors: They put down their pen and turn off their monitor. And doing the right thing gets great results. Their demonstrated care creates a strong emotional connection that unlocks 400 percent more discretionary effort.

Why does care elicit such a visceral response? Simple: It touches something vital inside us—our sense of worth. When self-worth is conferred, it can supercharge us. When it is denied, it can immobilize us.

Viktor Frankl endured and witnessed unspeakable beatings and tortures in Nazi prison camps. He discovered something fascinating about suffering and what really causes it. As devastating and debilitating as those physical beatings were, it was not the instrument of torture or the precision of its use that truly hurt. It was the complete lack of care about a person's worth.

The pain he caused me was not from any insults or any blows. That guard did not think it worth his while to say anything, not even a swear word, to the ragged, emaciated figure standing before him, which probably reminded him only vaguely of a human form. Instead, he playfully picked up a stone and threw it at me. That, to me, seemed the way to attract the attention of a beast, to call a domestic animal back to its job, a creature with which you have so little in common that you do not even punish it.*

It is the attack on the tortured person's self-worth that makes the torture unbearable. In contrast, leaders who demonstrate care for employees confer worth on them—the worth that makes even the toughest circumstances bearable.

"I'VE GOT YOUR BACK"

Sean Griffin is a staff sergeant who manages a platoon of police officers. His superior, Bruce, had instituted a vacation schedule that had caused considerable unrest among his employees. One of them, a talented young officer named Arun, was vocal in his opposition. Word got back to Bruce and he called Sean into his office.

"We're going to get rid of Arun," he said. "I don't put up with this kind of crap."

Sean went cold. He knew in that moment he was at a critical choice point: protect his career or his employee.

---

* Frankl, p. 24.

"You and I both know that you have the right and the power to make that call," Sean said, "but what's that going to do? It'll send out a clear message that anybody who speaks their truth won't last around here—that anybody who feels strongly about anything better stuff it and bury their thinking. I know this is suicide for my career, but I've got to stand up for Arun on this one, sir."

The meeting ended and Sean walked out thinking he had better prepare himself for a new posting.

A couple weeks later, one of Sean's colleagues took him aside. "You hear what Bruce did?"

Sean could just feel it coming, "No, but I can guess."

"No you can't. He changed the vacation schedule, basically implementing several of Arun's ideas. He told me, 'Griffin had the balls to stand up to me on this schedule thing. It bugged the hell out of me for a couple of days, but I came to the conclusion that he was right—and it's that kind of courage that I want to reward around here.'

"He said he's going to talk to you about it today. Oh, and all your employees heard about what went down. Arun told me, 'Griffin always told me that he had my back and I thought, yeah, whatever. But when I heard he put his future on the line, now I *know* he's got my back.' "

Do yourself a favor. Walk out your value for justice by doing the right thing for your employees in the middle of a highly political situation. Extending yourself in this way makes you a bigger person. Saying, "I've got your back" indicates that you care about your people, but risking your career *proves* you care. This kind of courageous care expresses your intentions like nothing else ever can.

Love is not a soft, fuzzy behavior exhibited by those who have no courage.

Love is placing worth on someone by demonstrating that you care about them as a person first and as an employee second.

CARE BUILDS SELF-WORTH

There was a guy in my hometown named Kenny who loved his cars. In fact it seemed as if he cared about cars more than anything else. He devoted considerable time washing, waxing, shampooing, and polishing them. Everybody in the whole town knew Kenny's cars were fine-tuned and immaculate. Many of them told him, "Kenny, if you ever think of selling that car, I want to be the first in line to buy it."

These people were willing to pay far more for Kenny's cars than a car of the same make, model, and year from anybody else. Why? Because they knew Kenny's cars were cared-for cars, and care confers worth on a car.

When you extend yourself to invest in the highest good of a person or an object, you increase the worth of that person or object. Just watch a teenager who has been well loved: She has a higher sense of self-worth. She won't easily allow others to mistreat her.

Love always places worth on its object. This means that how you see people is critical. Can you love someone you see as having no worth? No. You must see some form of worth in someone first.

I don't think that love *changes* a person's worth. I believe every person is irreplaceable and has inestimable worth. But I do have a hunch that love changes a person's *sense* of their worth.

I see this played out in organizations every day. For example, we do a lot of work in the health-care sector. I know CNOs (Chief Nursing Officers) who extend themselves to invest in the highest good of their nurses. They love them, support them, and care for them. Because these nurses feel cared for, they hold their heads high and are rarely targeted by bullies. Any physicians who mistreat one of these confident and secure nurses quickly discover steel and back off.

I know other CNOs who lack the courage to extend themselves and invest in the highest good of their nurses. Their lack of support essentially paints a bull's-eye on their employees. As a result, the employees seem to telegraph the message, "Disrespect me. Bully me. I'm worthless." And workplace bullies are only too happy to respond to those messages.

When employees feel you care, they care enough to offer their discretionary effort. Caring for someone's worth is what puts love into action. It won't change someone's worth but it will definitely change their sense of worth. And that simple change makes all the difference in their work experience.

LET MY PEOPLE GO SURFING!

In his book *Good Business* Mihaly Csikszentmihalyi highlights Yvon Chouinard of Patagonia as a leader who can teach us all something about creating moments of enjoyment:

> One of the happiest company headquarters I have ever visited is that of the outdoor equipment maker Patagonia, nestled in a set of recently refurbished factory buildings from the 1930s, in a sleepy neighborhood of Ventura, California. The entrance hallway is lined with surfboards that its employees have leaned against the wall. Yvon Chouinard describes the rationale behind this:
>
> > I'm a businessman, but I'm still going to do it on my own terms. I'm going to break a lot of rules and we're going to blur the distinction between work and play. So we have a policy here—it's called, "Let My People Go Surfing." A policy which is, when the surf comes up, anybody can just go surfing. Any time of the day, you can just take off and go surfing ... That attitude changes your whole life. If your life is set up so that you

can drop anything when the surf comes up, it changes the whole way you do your life. And it changed this whole company here.*

When you see this kind of policy, it's love at work, a clear sign that the leader cares about the enjoyment of his employees. But this policy telegraphs messages far beyond enjoyment. It clearly emits the signal, "We trust your judgment. We respect you as an adult."

How about you? What's your version of "Let My People Go Surfing"? If asked, would your employees be able to point to moments of enjoyment created by you as clear indicators that you care for their worth?

Perhaps you read the story above and perceive care as all syrup and no substance. I prefer to view care as a pragmatic concern for someone's highest good, a trait demonstrating that you give a rip about your employees. Yes, care can be ensuring that a new employee has someone to go out to lunch with every day of their first week, but it is just as likely to be a hard-nosed negotiation with the buyer of your business to make sure they will treat your employees right when they take over the reins.

Care seeks to create moments of enjoyment and delight for people, but, as you'll see, it fights for justice and fair treatment as well. Employees who experience this type of care feel like a million bucks.

---

* Csikszentmihalyi, *Good Business,* p. 109.

CARE SHARES THE WEALTH

In 1959, Bob Thompson and his wife, Ellen, scraped together their savings and started a paving company. Over forty dogged years, Bob developed the business until it became Michigan's largest paving empire.

Then, at the age of sixty-seven, in 1999, he decided to sell the business. But he decided he would sell only to a company that would guarantee the security and fair treatment of his employees. Thompson commented:

> Oldcastle was selected for more than price considerations. Their culture and demonstrated history of preserving existing management and business practices was of primary importance. I'm confident Oldcastle will continue the Thompson-McCully tradition of excellence.

With that agreement in place, Thompson signed a deal that would see him reaping the benefits of his hard work: He sold the company for $461 million.

So far the story could be that of any successful leader. But what happens next is truly intriguing.

Bob and Ellen Thompson not only ensured that their employees would not lose their jobs, they also made sure they wouldn't have to worry about it even if they did. They distributed $128 million to the employees who had helped them become successful. Employees with retirement plans received $2,000 for every year of service. Those without retirement plans received checks ranging from $1 million to $2 million, depending on length of service and merit.

"Our company's success has been due in large part to dedication and hard work of the men and women who have worked here over the years, and they deserve to be recognized ... You realize that the people around you have gone through all the pain and suffering with you ... I wanted to pay them back," Thompson said.

Gushy moment? Hardly. When the checks were handed out by his regional managers, Thompson was nowhere to be found.

"I didn't want to be there," he said. "It gets too emotional."

When Thompson's employees tell anecdotes about him it is clear he is no teddy bear. Getting called into his office was not a good thing. Yet when his wife, Ellen, sums him up, her description is of a man who exhibits both the hard and the soft. "He is hard-working and caring. I'm very proud of him," Ellen says.

THE LETTER

Typically, we love people the way we want to be loved. Seldom

---

* Hodges, "Robert Thompson: He Goes to the Head of the Class for Dedication to Help Educate Detroit Children."

do you find a leader who cares enough to discover how to love the employee the way he wants to be loved, but I know just such a leader in a global manufacturing organization. I've had the privilege of working with one of his direct reports for the past several years.

At the time of this particular story, Matthew, who is now the president of one of their divisions, was a senior vice president. He achieved the "A" rating right across the board in his performance review. That was almost impossible to achieve at the senior VP level of this company.

One day Matthew came home to find his wife, Jenny, reading a handwritten letter, tears streaming down her cheeks.

"Who's the letter from, honey?"

"It's from your boss Luke."

"Why are you crying?"

"He says in his letter that the 'A' rating is extremely hard to achieve and he goes on to explain the traits about you—apart from your results—that caused them to assign you this rating. Then he writes, 'Jenny, we are very clear that for Matthew to be able to achieve this rating, there is someone at home making great sacrifices. I want to thank you for your part in this.'"

I know that feeling valued and respected is a big energizer for Matthew. However, it matters to him who the respect comes from. He'd much rather feel the respect of his wife and his son than all the respect his colleagues can offer.

No one can go home and say to his wife and son, "I got the 'A' rating and here's why." You just can't do that. But your boss can do it for you.

Matthew knew that his boss cared, enough to make sure Jenny knew how valued he was at work and to make sure she felt valued and recognized for her contribution.

What impact do you think this kind of leadership had on Matthew? Do you think he had the power to make Luke look great? He did. The following year, Matthew grew his part of the business by $290 million.

This simply confirms what we already know: When value is felt, it releases the emotional engagement that unlocks discretionary effort. And discretionary effort produces great results.

Perhaps we can put to bed forever the myth that you have to be calculating and cerebral to be a great leader. Kouzes and Posner artfully address this myth in their book *Encouraging the Heart*. They cite a study conducted by the Center for Creative Leadership that focused on the factors that account for a manager's success. The surprising discovery was that there was only one factor that significantly differentiated the top-quartile managers from the bottom-quartile ones: higher scores on affection—both expressing it and desiring it.

Contrary to the myth of the cold-hearted boss who cares very little about people's feelings, the highest-performing managers show more warmth and fondness toward others than do the bottom 25 percent. They get closer to people, and they're significantly more open in sharing thoughts and feelings than their lower-performing counterparts.

Now these managers were not without their rational sides. In fact, on another measure administered by CCL they all scored high on "thinking," and on their need to have power and influence over others. It's just that these factors didn't explain why managers were higher performers.[*]

CLOSE THE FEELINGS GAP

I remember sitting in a meeting several years ago as the leader of the organization offered words of recognition and appreciation to one of his employees. There was one major problem: He was so focused on the wittiness and cleverness of his own presentation that the employee's achievement was diminished.

All of us were so grateful and proud of what this employee had

---

[*] Kouzes and Posner, pp. 9–10.

done, yet we walked away from this display of recognition feeling unfulfilled. Judging by the look on the employee's face, she felt that way, too.

I observed leaders of another organization hand out certificates to their star employees for successfully completing a challenging course. It should've been a moment of rich acknowledgment of their effort and commitment. It was the opposite. Too much was packed into the meeting. The certificates were handed out so quickly that it felt rushed and perfunctory. There was no time for the leaders to shake each person's hand, look them in the eye, congratulate them with a sincere thank you, and invite applause from the audience.

In both of these examples, leaders were trying to value their employees. However, they failed to close the feelings gap.

My business partner, Alex Somos, could teach leaders a lot in this matter. When he greets someone, he doesn't just say, "Good morning," he says, "Good morning. It's always so good to see you."

When he passes work to a colleague, he doesn't just say, "Can you look this over and get back to me with your feedback?" He says, "Can you look this over and get back to me with your feedback? Your thoughts always add value."

When he gives someone a gift, he doesn't just hand it to the person. He holds it up in both hands, pauses, looks the person directly in the eyes, and then presents it like a man offering an engagement ring to his fiancée.

When you're going to all the work of buying a gift, wrapping it up, and writing a card, why not extend another 10 percent of effort to make sure that all your work doesn't miss its mark? I will tell you from experience that the investment of that extra energy makes all the difference for Alex. His behavior leaves a singular imprint on his recipients. They feel profoundly cared for by him. I know—they have told me many times.

Closing the feelings gap will require you to extend yourself, especially if the person you are trying to love is very different from you. It may feel awkward or embarrassing the first few times. Naturally, you'll have to find ways that are consistent with your personality.

Every single day you expend energy in caring, by offering support, clarity, and recognition to your colleagues, your friends, and your family. Your intent to support, clarify, and recognize is not in question. The gap between your intent and your impact is.

How do you close the feelings gap? By caring. Leadership in the feelings economy not only gives you permission to care, it demands that you care if you're going to be successful. And the good news is that this investment of psychological capital is small compared with the return in emotional engagement.

Whether you are creating opportunities for people in a devastated market, giving an employee your undivided attention, going to bat for someone, creating "surfing" moments, or sharing the wealth, a moment of care can be the best part of your employee's day.

And as you'll soon see, care is anything but soft and fluffy.

10 | LOVE CHALLENGES PEOPLE TO STRETCH

Love at work happens when you
courageously step up with an unselfish
insistence that people
live up to their potential.

"Remember the power blackout of 2003?"

"Who could forget it? The way our employees pulled together was incredible. I wish I could bottle and sell whatever was going on inside them that week."

Whether it's the flood of 1999, the SARS outbreak of 2002, or the power blackout of 2003, the conversations all take on the same emotional tenor. It's not long before people become animated as they recall the intense dedication, sacrifice, cooperation, and off-the-charts performance of ordinary people turned extraordinary in the face of a daunting challenge.

A CHALLENGE PULLS OUT THE BEST

In fact, there is something inherent in the DNA of a challenge that pulls out the best in people. Challenges cause people to set aside their low-level thinking and rally toward the highest good. Maybe that's why we rise to them.

A challenge-less love is nice, but deficient. The leader who cares, nurtures, and serves but can't seem to challenge his employees has diminished his chances of achieving great results.

"I WANT TO KNOW THIS AFTERNOON"

Leaders who believe in people challenge them, with the kind of challenge that serves the highest good both of the individual and the organization. Max De Pree tells the story of a respected manager who matter-of-factly challenged people to high levels of accountability:

> One person whom I really admire recently called on somebody who hadn't been performing and said, "I'm going to give you three choices about your job." One, obviously, was to perform better. Another was to volunteer for a different job in the organization for which he might be better suited. The third was to retire early or go to another organization. And the employee said, "Fine, I'll think about that." The supervisor then asked, "How long are you going to think about it?" The reply was, "I was thinking maybe a month." The supervisor said, "I want to know this afternoon." This requirement wasn't cruel; it was taking into account the health of the organization.[*]

What a refreshingly direct approach. Do your people speak about you as the kind of leader who challenges them to achieve their highest potential? It's hard to claim that you care about your employees' worth if you are not challenging them to be as big as they can be.

Sheldon Sorge worked us harder than any of our other professors. He assigned work as if we were taking no other classes but his. Other professors took pity on us when we complained about our oppressive workload. Not Sheldon. He just kept piling it on.

---

[*]   De Pree, pp. 59–60.

Yet it was clear to us that he was interested in our highest good. He took the time to help us understand how each component of our curriculum would serve us later on. As a result, to this day, thirty years later, I can sit down and write out a score for a piece of music I am creating.

Visualize the face of the person who challenged you the most. The one who pushed you to the wall, who wouldn't let you get away with anything less than your best. At the time, you may have muttered "#&*$!#%" under your breath. Today, you look back with profound gratitude for the way this person invested in your highest good.

Susan's story illustrates how believing the best, patiently pulling out clarity, and serving someone's success can cause discomfort in the moment and appreciation in the long run.

> I started on a one-year contract as director of a badly demoralized IS group. They had just gone through a large failed project, were seeing senior management being let go, and were beginning to experience a restructuring that would see jobs go offshore and to the US.

> On my last day on the job a year later, one of my managers asked if he could have a moment alone with me. As the time approached, I dreaded what he was going to say.

> He started off by telling me that I had been hard on him, that I had told him things he didn't want to hear, and

that it had been difficult for him to come to terms with the fact that he wasn't as good as he thought. There were times in the past year when he hated me. But as time went by, he saw me working to get him the opportunities and coaching he needed to grow. He began to realize that I had his best interests at heart. He told me that when he was my age (we both laughed at that one) he would tell people that the person who had made the biggest difference in his career was me. What's more, he was going to ask for a demotion and go back to the operations area so he could get the business grounding that he felt he was still missing.

You see, he was a high flyer. Vice presidents loved him. Young, under thirty—he was told he was wonderful all his life, but he had no substance. The other managers who worked with him were down to earth—straight talkers— and barely tolerated him. My boss loved him.

Over the year there, I quietly worked away—giving facts and concerns—till the issues were laid bare. I did it in a supportive way, but there were hard messages that couldn't be shied from and there was at least one occasion when I was sure it would cost me my contract. But that last day made it all worthwhile.

As I said at the beginning of this book, love at work does not feed the narcissism epidemic; it squares off with it, holding people accountable to a higher form of contribution. But as we manage and lead millennials, it will serve us to be aware of two tendencies that can short-circuit our ability to challenge employees in a productive way. One is to avoid challenging people. The other is to challenge them only as a means of getting our own ego needs met. Some of us will require more courage, others more selflessness.

Love at work does not feed narcissism.

Love at work squares off with narcissism.

Love at work happens when you courageously step up with an unselfish insistence that people live up to their potential.

STRETCH THE BEST AND YOU GROW THE BEST

Buckingham and Coffman tell a great story in *First, Break All the Rules* that shows how stretching high performers grows your organizational capacity.

> When it comes to data entry roles, the average employee performs at a level of 19,000 keypunches per day, or 380,000 per month. If you are a talented manager you should be able to challenge a new data entry employee to stretch her performance beyond this national average of 380,000 keypunches.

How much do you think you could improve someone's performance? Twenty-five percent? Thirty? Fifty? If you had an employee who was already performing at a level 50 percent higher than the national average, what would you do? You might be surprised but challenged to discover that the best data entry employees surpass the national average by 1,000 percent.

Jean P. is one such employee. When she was first measured, she averaged 560,000 punches per month, already 50 percent above the national average. She was recognized for her performance, then she and her manager set out some individual goals that could help her improve and track her performance. Three months later she hit a million keypunches … Today Jean's personal best is 3,526,000 keypunches in a month, and the average of all the data entry employees working around her is over a million.*

What is the highest good? What is someone's best? How far do you stretch someone? This story challenges our preconceived notions of what's possible. It would be easy to look at Jean's monthly average of 560,000 keypunches, recognize her for her great work, and hesitate to ask for more. But taking that approach would rob her of the joy of being in flow and sub-optimize the productivity of everyone around her.

Every time you notice someone doing a great job, remember

---

* Buckingham, Marcus and Curt Coffman. *First, Break All the Rules*, p. 161.

that top performers have the most potential for growth and the greatest capacity to stretch their co-workers.

WHO NEEDS TO BE CHALLENGED?

The percentage of superstars in any given organization is not high. The greater percentage is made up of people with varying degrees of talent, motivation, and commitment.

You are working primarily with a group of people who are doing their level best to juggle the demands of a busy home life, keep healthy while wading through a virus soup, hold their financial troubles at bay, and find any way possible to adapt to an ever-changing workplace dynamic. Your job is to be the alchemist who can produce gold from everyday ore, achieving superstar results through everyday people. In Greenleaf's words:

> It is part of the enigma of human nature that the "typical" person ... is capable of great dedication and heroism *if* he or she is wisely led. Many otherwise able people are disqualified to lead because they cannot work with and through the half-people who are all there are. The secret of institution building is to be able to weld a team of such people by lifting them up to grow taller than they would otherwise be.[*]

Lifting people up to grow taller is the noblest kind of challenge.

---

[*]   Greenleaf, p. 35.

It demands the courage and grit that will extend you as a leader.

LOVE MAKES PEOPLE STRONG

Want your abs, calves, or biceps to grow? Here's how to make it happen.

First you exert yourself far beyond your comfort zone to the point of stress, tearing the micro-fibers of your muscles. Then you rest your muscles over the next couple of days so the fibers can recover and repair themselves.

This is the cycle that creates the growth of muscles: Stress and recovery, stress and recovery, stress and recovery. (For more on this concept read *The Power of Full Engagement* by Jim Loehr and Tony Schwartz.)

I do not subscribe to the concept of work–life balance. I do subscribe to the concept of work–life *integration*. Let's be honest about the way life really works. There are seasons when you just have to drive to achieve a result. There are other seasons when it's time to back off and take a break.

Consider the implications of this stress–recovery model in managing people. Part of our workforce, the millennials, know all about recovery, but don't stress their psychological muscles enough to tear them. Another part of our workforce, the boomers, know all about the stress part, they just know nothing about recovery.

Recovery without stress will never make you strong. Neither will stress without recovery. Our job as leaders is to help people integrate the two in ways that make them grow and flourish.

We can do our employees a big favor by managing their expectations and teaching them this principle. We can say, "Every day is not going to look the same for you here. The peaks and valleys of the marketplace just don't allow for that. There will be days and even weeks when we need you to drive very hard. There will be other times when we will expect you to take a break. As leaders, we will be trustworthy by not only giving you the break but demanding that you take it to recover from the times of stress."

Here's the point: Love challenges people to stretch to the point of tearing the muscles. So courageously step into that spot. See the potential of your organization, expect the best, and pull it out by challenging everyone to do more than they believe is possible.

THE STRANGE ATTRACTOR

Identifying an intrinsic vision that is compelling enough to win people's sacrifice is part of the work of leadership. In particular, what is required is cooperating with and triggering what chaos theory proponents call "the strange attractor." Dr. Stephen Covey shares his insights on this in his preface to Greenleaf's book *Servant Leadership.*

The strange attractor is a sense of vision that people are drawn to, and united in, that enables them to be driven by motivation inside them toward achieving a common purpose.*

At the beginning of this chapter we looked at the herculean effort given by employees in the midst of blackouts, floods, and SARS outbreaks. The strange attractor has the chemical makeup from those circumstances that we'd love to bottle and sell: a universal challenge that catalyzes people's noblest efforts.

However, love doesn't sit around on its hands waiting for a blackout or a flood. It disrupts the status quo and points the way for people to engage in a higher, universal purpose. I believe most North Americans—especially our millennials—are drowning in freedom but starving for purpose. Great leaders harness this latent energy and stretch people to do something truly meaningful.

As Kouzes and Posner put it, "When it comes to excellence, it's definitely not 'What gets rewarded gets done,' it's 'What is rewarding gets done.' "**

So identifying the universal purpose of your organization is critical. Marcus Buckingham unpacks the notion of universal purpose brilliantly in his book *The One Thing You Need to Know*. He compares the game of checkers with the game of chess. In checkers, the pieces all move in the same fashion; in chess, each piece moves in its own unique way. Which do you think leaders play: checkers or chess?

---

*   Greenleaf, p. 3.
**   Kouzes and Posner, p. 174.

As I went through Buckingham's work I was surprised to discover that leaders play checkers and managers play chess. Buckingham points out that leaders tap into the universal purpose—the one thing that moves people—while managers identify the unique talents of each individual player and place them in a role that showcases those moves.

Both skills are important in different situations for different reasons. But in your role as leader you can unlock the power of the strange attractor by identifying the universal purpose of your organization and rallying people around it. In a hospital, this may be compassionate care; in law enforcement, justice; in retail, service; in manufacturing, quality. Do what it takes to know what it is for your organization.

BUT AREN'T PEOPLE SELF-MOTIVATED?

Last winter I was training to run a marathon. There were two leaders in my running group, one about my age and the other much younger, probably in his late twenties. We were at the end of a twenty-four-kilometer run and were approaching one of Guelph's steepest hills. My knee had been giving me pain from a prolonged injury, and as we approached the hill, I slowed to a walk. The fifty-year-old leader ran up to me and asked, "You okay?"

"Yep. I just need to rest my knee."

"Okay. Just do what you need to do."

Then the young leader ran up to me and said, "What are you doing?"

"I'm just giving my knee a break."

"Oh no you're not. Come on, keep running."

"No, you go ahead. I'm okay."

"No. You're running the hill. Come on."

"I'm exhausted. I can't go any farther. You go ahead."

"You're running the frickin' hill! Now come with me!"

With this young man's "encouragement" and goading, I ran the entire way up the hill. I felt exultant as my running mates stood at the top and applauded me.

Later, I realized that, while the older leader had empathy for me, the young leader was not burdened by any empathy at all. He remembered my telling him that I had a tendency to shut down close to the end of a race and wasn't having any of it.

I'm a pretty self-motivated guy. But I would not have lived up to my potential without the extrinsic motivation of my young friend's gritty challenge.

Daniel Pink's book *Drive* clearly lays out the power of intrinsic

> **Love is not** challenging to affirm your identity
> as a challenger or to get your needs met.
>
> **Love is** challenging to ignite the belief, passion,
> and commitment that your people need
> to fulfill **their** true potential.

motivators. Like him, I believe the most powerful and sustainable form of motivation is intrinsic. If that's true, the leader's challenge is basically an inside-out job: pulling out what is most important to the employee. But there is an equally powerful truth: Even the most self-motivated employees can be ignited by healthy extrinsic motivators, such as a clear, compelling picture of the future, or a rallying cry to grapple with an audacious goal. Loving leaders tap into the intent of their employees and challenge any behavior that could torpedo that intent.

AFFIRM THE INTENTION— ADDRESS THE IMPACT

Challenging people is a critical leadership skill, but you'll get into trouble if you challenge the wrong thing. Blair Steinbach is an emotional intelligence expert who has had a significant impact on the international business community. He threw out a little seed to a group of people one day that has begun to grow into something substantial for me. "When you're in a tough conversation," he said, "affirm the intention and address the impact."

We often get this mixed up and address people's intentions.

This makes it easy for them to discount the validity of our challenge. Here are some examples of how to do this skill:

* "Raj, I can see your intention is to create a spike in productivity. What sort of impact did it have on people when you started raising your voice in the meeting?"

* "Rosetta, I believe your intention is to help me be successful. Can we talk about the impact it had on me when you just handed me my goals, rather than working through them with me?"

* "Your intention to recognize your salespeople's efforts seemed clear to me, Sharon. What I want to discuss with you is the impact it had on my team when they discovered they weren't getting any credit for their part in your team's success."

CHALLENGE: THE PROOF THAT YOU BELIEVE

When you truly believe in someone, you naturally challenge her. But love that challenges makes sure the recipient feels challenged to reach their highest good, not simply to satisfy the whim of the challenger.

Love expends the effort so the challenge comes across in a way that conveys belief, pull, service, and care. In this way, love's five actions always operate in an integrated fashion, rather than in isolation from one another.

11 LOVE YOUR SELF

Your job is to be the alchemist who can produce gold from everyday ore, achieving superstar results through everyday people.

At this point you may be asking yourself, "Where do I get the energy to love like this?" You probably have no quarrel with the concepts of believing in someone's highest good, trying to pull it out, serve it, care for it, and challenge it. But you may not be so sure about where you will get the energy to do it. Here's where it's critical to learn to love your self.

SELFISHNESS VS. SELF-LOVE

It felt like a knife entered my heart today. We packed up a few of my Mom's favorite things, left the home she has lived in and loved for sixty years, and moved her to Manitoulin Lodge, an extended care facility in her hometown of Gore Bay.

Once there, we unpacked her belongings in her room. I watched Mom as she spunkily introduced herself to her roommate. The response was a loud, high-pitched moan. I cringed. Mom tried to put a brave face on it, but I knew she was thinking there'd be no engaging conversations here. I tried not to cry. I wish we could have found a different way.

My wife had offered to quit her job so we could bring Mom to live with us in Guelph, but Mom's entire social network for the past sixty years has been in Gore Bay. Plucking her out of that network would be unkind.

My brother, Perry, had hoped to sell his optometric practice, buy Mom's house, and have her live with him. No luck there.

My siblings and I tried finding caregivers who could live with Mom but were unsuccessful. And leaving her in her own home was no longer an option. None of us can bear the thought of Mom electrocuted, scarred by a burn, or lying crumpled at the bottom of the stairs.

All this bubbled to the surface when I arrived for a six-week stay on the island. I had come with two specific mandates from my organization: (1) Get rejuvenated from the blistering pace of the last year, and (2) Write your next book. But upon arrival, I learned that Mom needed to be shifted to more intensive care than she had been receiving.

So I faced a dicey choice point hundreds of times during this time: love my mom, or love myself.

The answer sounds easy, right? "Psssst, your mom, idiot! Your mom!"

In theory, that is the easy choice. In practice, it's not so easy. I have to manage the tension between several sets of powerfully opposing needs. I am responsible to my business partner, to my employees, to my family, to my siblings, to myself, as well as to my mother. In fact, setting aside my own needs to consistently meet the needs of my mother is not only unrealistic, it's also not love, because it's not healthy for her.

Let me pose this question to you: At what point does self-love (which is healthy) become selfishness (which is unhealthy)?

In the past, I have simply denied my own needs and accommodated the needs of the other person. This eased tension and made me feel altruistic—quite loving, in fact. But energy was lost in the process. Love draws its energy from living in the tension between our own needs and another's needs. When we buckle to one or the other, we miss out on loving ourselves and aren't really loving the other, either.

I consider Erich Fromm to be a master on the subject of self-love. I want to honor his thinking extensively in this chapter. The following words from him accurately capture my past tendencies.

> The "unselfish" person "does not want anything for himself"; he "lives only for others," is proud that he does not consider himself important. He is puzzled to find that in spite of his unselfishness he is unhappy, and that his relationships to those closest to him are unsatisfactory ... Behind the façade of unselfishness a subtle but not less intense self-centeredness is hidden.*

What is the difference between selfishness and self-love? How does selfishness manifest itself? Fromm goes on to explain:

> *Selfishness and self-love, far from being identical, are actually opposites.* The selfish person does not love himself too much but too little; in fact he hates himself. This lack of

---

* Fromm, p. 57.

fondness and care for himself, which is only one expression of his lack of productiveness, leaves him empty and frustrated. He is necessarily unhappy and anxiously concerned to snatch from life the satisfactions which he blocks himself from attaining. He seems to care too much for himself, but actually he only makes an unsuccessful attempt to cover up and compensate for his failure to care for his real self ... *It is true that selfish persons are incapable of loving others, but they are not capable of loving themselves either.*

WE LEARN TO HATE OURSELVES

I learned the rules of life from my family as I grew up. I was the fourth-born boy of five children. Unfortunately, I was a naughty, stubborn, bratty little guy who was very difficult to love. I learned soon enough that I was not lovable for who I was. I was lovable only if I performed in a certain way.

Because performing well was difficult for me, I figured I must be somehow defective or damaged. But when my mother scolded me and I felt ashamed, then the world seemed to make sense. As I felt her disgust, everything seemed to add up: I wasn't worth the effort to correct or discipline, but I needed to be shown that I was inappropriate.

When I hit the age of twelve I began to destroy myself with alcohol and drugs, and for good reason: I hated me. Self-destruction was my way of obeying all the rules that life had taught me:

---

*   Fromm, p. 56.

* I'm a liar. I should be judged and punished.

* I'm a thief. I should be shamed and scolded.

* I'm bad. I'm worthy of contempt.

* I'm a drug addict. I should be despised.

Fast-forward many years to the 1990s. I had a wife and four children. What were the chances that I'd be able to extend myself to invest in their highest good?

Although I tried my best to be encouraging and affirming, my harsh and judgmental attitude toward myself caused a silent stream of disappointment and judgment to seep out of me toward Theresa and the kids. Although I wanted my kids to thrive, my belief that I wasn't worthy to be held accountable to be the best I could be caused me to fail to challenge them to be all *they* could be. In short, despite my desire and commitment to love, I was unable to love others in the exact areas in which I could not love myself.

Meister Eckhart sums it up this way: "If you love yourself, you love everybody else as you do yourself."

Loving those who love you takes no special effort or talent. Loving your offspring is natural: Even animals do that. It's loving your enemies that stretches you the most, especially the

181

ones who hate you. The person who despises you most consistently and most intimately is you. That's why love's curriculum starts with you first.

Once again, Fromm's insights are helpful:

> Not only others, but we ourselves are the "object" of our feelings and attitudes; the attitudes toward others and toward ourselves, far from being contradictory, are basically conjunctive ... love of others and love for ourselves are not alternatives. On the contrary, an attitude of love toward themselves will be found in all those who are capable of loving others ... If an individual is able to love productively, he loves himself too; if he can love only others, he can not love at all.[*]

FIVE WAYS TO LOVE YOUR SELF

Many people need to be loved by you, and you are one of them. From an objective point of view, your needs are as valid as the needs of your siblings, parents, children, friends, co-workers, or spouse.

In fact, if your love needs continue to go unmet, you will become less useful in meeting others' love needs.

So let's look at five ways you can begin to extend your self

---

[*] Fromm, pp. 55–56.

to invest in the highest good of a person who really needs it: your self.

1. Believe in your self: identify potentialities

2. Engage in a dialogue: pull out the assignment

3. Serve your self: set your intention

4. Care for your self: affirm your intentions

5. Challenge your self: address your impact

BELIEVE IN YOUR SELF: IDENTIFY POTENTIALITIES

What would happen if you began to apply everything you read in chapter 6 ("Love Believes in People") to your self? What would happen if you began to expect the best from your self? What if you spent time exploring the essential traits and features about your self: those things that make you distinctly you? What if you began to ask: "What are the potentialities in me that are waiting to be actualized?"

Here is a question that I frequently ask myself, and I encourage you to do the same: "What is the highest end to which my life can be used in this world?" Asking questions like this opens up the possibility of a powerful self-dialogue.

ENGAGE IN A DIALOGUE:
PULL OUT THE ASSIGNMENT

As we've discovered, love pulls rather than pushes. It comes alongside with a blend of intense curiosity and refreshing directness and starts by pulling out the other person's reality. You do this for others, so why wouldn't you do it for your self? Engage your self in dialogue and ask, "Okay, if these are my potentialities, what concrete assignment is life is asking me to actualize?"

Listen intently without judging, criticizing, or offering advice. After you have shared your own reality, reflect back the implications of what the assignment means inside your world. Ask your self, "So what gets in the way for you?" and "If you were to try to action this, how might you go about it?" In this self-coaching phase, your goal is to make your self feel completely understood. Once you do, you will be energized to serve.

SERVE YOUR SELF:
BROADCAST YOUR INTENTION

You've believed the best of your self, engaged in dialogue, and discovered the concrete assignment that life is asking you to actualize. Now it is critical for you to serve your self by crystallizing this assignment into a goal: a clear, mental picture of what you want to achieve. You need to help your self do three simple things with this clear mental picture:

1. Write it down as a goal.

2. Go back to it frequently and hold it in your mind.

3. Cultivate a stance of positive expectation toward its fulfillment.

When you do these three things, you broadcast your intention to the entire world. This begins to remove interference and aligns life's circumstances to come and serve your goal. As you work and wait for your goal's achievement, it will be crucial for you to care for your intentions along the way.

CARE FOR YOUR SELF: AFFIRM YOUR INTENTIONS

You've believed the best, pulled out life's assignment, and broadcast it to the world. Now, to go the full distance, your self needs to know its worth. Here's where caring for your self comes in.

One of the best ways to care for your self is the simple act of affirmation. You need to know that it is not only okay to affirm your self, it is vitally necessary to do so. Whether you admit to it or not, you need affirmation the same way you need oxygen. It is a legitimate human need. The problem is, the people you live with and work with may not know how to do this capably. So don't leave the fulfillment of this basic human need to chance. Make affirming your self a discipline.

Perhaps this notion of affirming your self makes you bristle. Remember, the selfish person loves himself not too much but too little. We would do well to take Blair Steinbach's advice: "Take care of you so there is more of you to take care of the world."

> **The selfish person** doesn't love himself too much.
>
> **The selfish person** loves himself too little.

Take your self out for a walk. Address your self by name. I might do it this way: "Brady, I know you feel bad that the present you got for your wife was a flop. You wanted to surprise her with the perfect gift but it just didn't turn out that way. I affirm who you are at the core, Brady. Your intentions are good. You *are* a good husband."

You would do this for your kids. You would do it for your partner. You would do it for a friend. You can't honestly say you are loving your self if you won't do this for you. And lest you get the impression that care equals coddling, let's move into the ways in which care will step up to challenge you.

CHALLENGE YOUR SELF: QUESTION THE IMPACT

When you do not live up to your potential and act in ways that subvert your intentions, it's time to challenge your self by addressing the impact of your behaviors.

"So Brady, I know your intention is to love Theresa and be a great husband for her. I'm not questioning your intention at all. I do want to ask you, what sort of impact does it have on Theresa when you become reserved and detached? Do you think she is clear on why you are acting that way? If she's not, what emotions will that lack of clarity stir up within her? I know it is not your intention for her to feel uncared for; that's just not the kind of husband you want to be. So what are you going to do about this?"

Get the picture? Love affirms the intentions and addresses the impact.

As I found with my mom this summer, life offers many choice points. You ask your self, "What's the right thing to do here? Is this selfishness or self-love?" Your ability to distinguish between the two will enable you to do the right thing in the moment.

12 | WHAT'S YOUR SOURCE?

The world's greatest source of
renewable energy is not geothermal.
Nor is it solar, wind, or tide.
The world's greatest source of
renewable energy is love.

Extending your self to invest in another's highest good is a taxing order. The energy required to believe in someone, pull out their highest good, serve their success, care for their worth, and challenge them to stretch will exhaust you, deplete you, and bring you to the end of yourself.

Let me pose a question to you, then: "Where will you get the energy to lead like this? What is your energy source?"

I'm going to be vulnerable with you at this point and share the spiritual operating system that energizes my love. I have learned that I can count on four fuel sources to energize my love: God, others, self, and recovery.

GOD

I hear a lot of people saying they know God. I don't know much about God. I have been left unfulfilled in this regard—and it's not for lack of making my desires known.

Here's an ongoing conversation that God and I share.

Brady: "So I've heard it said that it's possible to know you—to actually experience you and know you like I know my best friend."

God: (Silence)

Brady: "Yeah, so, I know what my friend Alex's voice sounds

191

like. I'd love to hear what your voice sounds like." (At this point I strain to listen.)

God: (Silence)

Brady: "I know what Alex's face looks like; what color his eyes are. I'd love to see your face." (I try to conjure up some kind of image of God's face.)

God: (Silence)

You get the picture. The conversation goes on and on like this with me over-trying to know God the way I know my wife, Theresa, or my friend, Alex. You can see that the God relationship has been a challenge for me, but I don't want to leave you with the wrong impression. I've experienced God's support for me in difficult moments. I can see how God has used circumstances to direct me. I have felt God drop the perfect ideas and resources into my lap at just the right moments.

However, the best bits for me are the moments in which I realize how God feels about me. Sometimes I'll be driving down the road in my car thinking, "I wonder how Robin's hip is coming along. I should call her and let her know I'm thinking about her. And I'm going to send an e-mail off to Jay to see if he needs help moving."

I stop and think, "Why am I thinking about the needs of these people when I have so many other things clamoring for my attention?" It's then that my attention is drawn to a recent experience of having felt loved by God: a moment when I had the sensation that God was actually fond of me, a moment in which I felt like I was God's child. This love, when felt, always produces the same result: I begin to initiate love toward others.

The world's greatest source of renewable energy is not geo-thermal. Nor is it solar, wind, or tide. The world's greatest source of renewable energy is love. I don't know what your primary source of love is, but I hope that you have discovered something akin to this—something that refills your depleted love batteries and energizes you to keep loving.

OTHERS

One of the primary ways our love batteries are recharged is by the love that comes into our lives through others.

This has been a tremendous challenge for me. I grew up with the credo that love is not receiving from others; it is giving to others. I have hundreds of memories of my dad paying for the dinner of up to three to four families at a restaurant. He would simply pull out his wallet and take care of it. Others sometimes objected, but my dad always picked up the tab.

Mom and Dad were always the ones initiating, serving, giving, and opening up our home to others. A message was put into me, bone deep: You're a good person when you give; you're inferior when you have to receive.

It took me almost half a century to come to a different con-clusion. To the extent that I do not allow others to meet my needs, I fail to honor them and love them. Love is not individu-alism. Love is not independence. Love is not self-reliance. Love is a dance of reciprocity: giving at one time and receiving at another. I cannot call myself a loving person if I will not receive from others.

> **Love is not** individualism, independence, or self-reliance.
>
> **Love is** a dance of reciprocity.

When you have plenty, your responsibility is to ask how you can help. When you lack, your responsibility is to make your needs known. Learn to receive energy from the encouragement, affir-mation, friendship, and loving acts of others.

SELF

I covered loving self in the previous chapter. Suffice it to say that loving your self not only makes you eligible to love others, it also refills your love batteries so you have the energy to invest in others.

RECOVERY

Your muscles grow only during recovery. That's when the body goes to work to repair the torn muscle fibers. Yes, you have to tear the muscles or there is no rebuilding. Growth happens only in recovery. So when you're thinking about recharging your love batteries, be sure to schedule recovery time for yourself into your calendar. You'll need that after a season of extending yourself to love others.

Learn to tap into these four fuel sources so you can love for the long haul. There's a better world to be built, and a legacy for you to leave. Doing so will demand all the energy you can allow to pass through you.

13 | BUILD A BETTER WORLD

Let's do the right thing. Let's start a revolution of love at work.

You are leaving a legacy. You may not have visualized what that legacy is. You may not have written it down anywhere. You may not even be aware of it. But make no mistake, you are leaving one. People will remember your imprint. You get to choose: Will you leave a legacy of love or of something else?

Some leaders will leave a legacy of fear. Some a legacy of niceness. Others a legacy of avoidance. You get to choose what your legacy will be.

My goal in writing this book was to incite you to love your people. If I can get enough leaders doing this, we will build a better world.

* Erin Feuerstein challenged CEOs to do what's right for their people when he rebuilt his factory and paid wages to his workers for three months.

* Bob Thompson raised the bar on what it means to share your wealth with the employees who help you create it.

* Dr. Dean Ornish has set a new standard in the health-care field for how we deal with heart patients.

* Dr. Mimi Silbert has shown all of us what's possible when it comes to transforming criminals into productive citizens.

I'm not sure any political leader can accomplish these things. I'm quite certain there isn't one particular country that can accomplish them. But there is one entity that has the reach and influence to build a better world: the loving organization.

Unlike political leaders, or powerful countries, organizations can go anywhere and influence almost anyone. Imagine a world with me, a world in which every hotel chain, every relief organization, every news agency, every software company, every school, every mosque, every church, and every synagogue existed to love people and seek their highest good.

What fractures could be healed?

What world-changing innovations could be spawned?

What chasms could be crossed?

What disasters could be averted?

What would it be like to live in this kind of world?

It may be that only our great grandchildren will know. But perhaps by bringing love into our organizations, we will facilitate a more rapid transformation: one in which our grandchildren will delight our aging ears with the stories of astonishing alternate forms of energy, mediation tools of Gaza Strip proportions, health-care systems that make us vibrant, the abolishment of childhood poverty and slavery, justice systems that bring restitution and restoration, and education systems that unleash the finest potentialities of every child.

It is time for these things. It is time to build a better world. Let's do the right thing. Let's start a revolution of love at work.

BIBLIOGRAPHY

So many great authors have shaped my thinking and therefore this book, *Love at Work*. This bibliography acknowledges my respect and gratitude to them and gives you a window into the types of thinkers who have informed my work.

BOOKS

Adams, Marilee G. *Change Your Questions, Change Your Life: 7 Powerful Rules for Life and Work*. San Francisco: Berrett-Koehler, 2004.

Ayers, Keith E. *Engagement Is Not Enough: You Need Passionate Employees To Achieve Your Dream*. Charleston: Advantage Media Group, 2006.

Bachrach, Bill and Karen Risch (eds.) *Values-Based Selling: The Art of Building High-Trust Client Relationships*. San Diego: Bachrach & Associates, 1996.

Baker, Dan. *What Happy People Know: How the New Science of Happiness Can Change Your Life for the Better*. New York: St. Martin's Griffin, 2004.

Barrett, Richard. *Liberating the Corporate Soul: Building a Visionary Organization*. Woburn, MA: Butterworth-Heinemann, 1998.

Bartholomew, Kathleen. *Ending Nurse-to-Nurse Hostility: Why Nurses Eat Their Young and Each Other*. Marblehead, MA: HCPro, 2006.

Bibliography

Bohm, David. *On Dialogue*. London and New York: Routledge, 1996.

Bradberry, Travis and Jean Greaves. *The Emotional Intelligence Quick Book: Everything You Need to Know to Put Your EQ to Work*. New York: TalentSmart, 2003.

Bridges, William. *The Way of Transition: Embracing Life's Most Difficult Moments*. Cambridge, MA: Perseus, 2001.

Buckingham, Marcus. *The One Thing You Need to Know … About Great Managing, Great Leading, and Sustained Individual Success*. New York: Free Press, 2005.

Buckingham, Marcus and Curt Coffman. *First, Break All the Rules: What the World's Greatest Managers Do Differently*. New York: Simon & Schuster, 1999.

Campbell, Ross. *How to Really Love Your Child*. Wheaton: Victor Books, 1977.

Cashman, Kevin. *Leadership from the Inside Out: Becoming a Leader for Life*. Minneapolis: LeaderSource, 1998.

Chapman, Gary. *Love as a Way of Life: Seven Keys to Transforming Every Aspect of Your Life*. Colorado Springs: WaterBrook Press, 2008.

Cialdini, Robert. *Influence: The Psychology of Persuasion*. New York: Quill, 1994.

Clarke, Boyd and Ron Crossland. *The Leader's Voice: How Your Communication Can Inspire Action and Get Results!* New York: SelectBooks, 2002.

Coens, Tom and Mary Jenkins. *Abolishing Performance Appraisals: Why They Backfire and What to Do Instead*. San Francisco: Berrett-Koehler, 2000.

Collins, Jim. *Good to Great: Why Some Companies Make the Leap … And Others Don't*. New York: HarperCollins, 2001.

Collins, Jim and Jerry I. Porras. *Built to Last: Successful Habits of Visionary Companies*. New York: HarperBusiness, 1997.

Connellan, Thomas K. *Bringing Out the Best in Others!: 3 Keys for Business Leaders, Educators, Coaches and Parents*. Austin: Bard Press, 2003.

Bibliography

Crabb, Larry. *Connecting: Healing Ourselves and Our Relationships.* Nashville: Word, 1997.

Csikszentmihalyi, Mihaly. *Good Business: Leadership, Flow, and the Making of Meaning.* New York: Penguin, 2004

Csikszentmihalyi, Mihaly. *Flow: The Psychology of Optimal Experience.* New York: HarperPerennial, 1990.

Curran, Charles A. *Understanding: A Necessary Ingredient in Human Belonging.* Chicago: Apple River Press, 1978.

Daniels, Aubrey C. *Bringing Out the Best in People: How to Apply the Astonishing Power of Positive Reinforcement.* New York: McGraw-Hill, 2000.

Denning, Stephen. *The Springboard: How Storytelling Ignites Action in Knowledge-Era Organizations.* Butterworth-Heinemann, 2000.

De Pree, Max. *Leading Without Power: Finding Hope in Serving Community.* San Francisco: Jossey-Bass, 2003.

Deutschman, Alan. *Change or Die: Could You Change When Change Matters Most?* New York: HarperCollins, 2008.

Ellinor, Linda and Glenna Gerard. *Dialogue: Rediscover the Transforming Power of Conversation.* New York: Wiley, 1998.

Faber, Adele and Elaine Mazlish. *How to Talk So Kids Will Listen and Listen So Kids Will Talk.* New York: Avon Books, 1980.

Fadiman, James and Robert Frager. *Essential Sufism.* San Francisco: HarperSanFrancisco, 1997.

Fisher, Roger, William Ury, and Bruce Patton. *Getting to Yes: Negotiating Agreement Without Giving In.* New York: Penguin, 1991.

Frankl, Victor E. *Man's Search for Meaning: An Introduction to Logotherapy.* Boston: Beacon Press, 2006.

Fromm, Erich. *The Art of Loving.* New York: HarperCollins, 2006.

Frost, Peter J. *Toxic Emotions at Work: How Compassionate Managers Handle Pain and Conflict.* Boston: Harvard Business School Press, 2003.

Gallwey, W. Timothy. *The Inner Game of Work: Focus, Learning,*

Pleasure, and Mobility in the Workplace. New York: Random House, 2000.

Garfield, Charles. *Peak Performers: The New Heroes of American Business*. New York: Avon Books, 1987.

Gladwell, Malcolm. *Blink: The Power of Thinking Without Thinking*. New York: Little, Brown, 2005.

Gladwell, Malcolm. *Outliers: The Story of Success*. New York: Little, Brown, 2008.

Goldstein, Noah J., Steve J. Martin, and Robert B. Cialdini. *Yes!: 50 Scientifically Proven Ways to Be Persuasive*. New York: Free Press, 2008.

Goleman, Daniel. *Working with Emotional Intelligence*. New York: Bantam Books, 1998.

Goleman, Daniel, Richard Boyatzis, and Annie McKee. *Primal Leadership: Learning to Lead with Emotional Intelligence*. Boston: Harvard Business School Press, 2002.

Goleman, Daniel. *Social Intelligence: The New Science of Human Relationships*. New York: Random House, 2006.

Gottman, John and Nan Silver. *The Seven Principles for Making Marriage Work*. New York: Crown, 1999.

Greenleaf, Robert K. *Servant Leadership: A Journey into the Nature of Legitimate Power and Greatness*. Mahwah, NJ: Paulist Press, 2002.

Habashy, Baha and Margaret Habashy. *Overloaded? From Overload to Balanced Living: Taking Control of Work and Information Overload*. Markham, ON: Integrity+, 2004.

Harper, Gary. *The Joy of Conflict Resolution: Transforming Victims, Villains, and Heroes in the Workplace and at Home*. Gabriola Island, BC: New Society Publishers, 2004.

Hendricks, Gay and Kathleen Hendricks. *Conscious Loving: The Journey to Co-Commitment*. New York: Bantam Books, 1990.

Hesse, Hermann. *The Journey to the East*. London: Paladin Books, 1989.

Hurtig, Mel. *The Truth About Canada: Some Important, Some*

Astonishing, And Some Truly Appalling Things All Canadian Should Know About Our Country. Toronto: Emblem, McClelland and Stewart, 2008.

Irvine, David and Jim Reger. *The Authentic Leader: It's About Presence, Not Position.* Sanford, FL: DC Press, 2006.

Isaacs, William. *Dialogue: The Art of Thinking Together.* New York: Doubleday, 1999.

Janov, Jill. *The Inventive Organization: Hope and Daring at Work.* San Francisco: Jossey-Bass, 1994.

Kahane, Adam. *Solving Tough Problems: An Open Way of Talking, Listening, and Creating New Realities.* San Francisco: Berrett-Koehler, 2004.

Kaplan, Robert S. and David P. Norton. *Alignment: Using the Balanced Scorecard to Create Corporate Synergies.* Boston: Harvard Business School Press, 2006.

Katzenbach, Jon R. and Douglas K. Smith. *The Wisdom of Teams: Creating the High-Performance Organization.* New York: McKinsey & Company, 2003.

Kaye, Beverly and Sharon Jordan-Evans. *Love 'em or Lose 'em: Getting Good People to Stay.* San Fransisco: Berrett-Koehler, 2005.

Kelley, Matthew. *The Dream Manager.* New York: Beacon Publishing, 2007.

Kohn, Alfie. *Punished by Rewards: The Trouble with Gold Stars, Incentive Plans, As, Praise, and Other Bribes.* New York: Houghton Mifflin, 1993.

Kotter, John P. and Dan S. Cohen. *The Heart of Change: Real Life Stories of How People Change Their Organizations.* Boston: Harvard Business School Press, 2002.

Kouzes, James M. and Barry Z. Posner. *Encouraging the Heart: A Leader's Guide to Rewarding and Recognizing Others.* San Francisco: Jossey-Bass, 2003.

Kouzes, James M. and Barry Z. Posner. *The Leadership Challenge.* San Francisco: Jossey-Bass, 2007.

Kraybill, Ronald S. with Robert A. Evans and Alice Frazer Evans. *Peace Skills: Manual for Community Mediators*. San Francisco: Jossey-Bass, 2001.

Laney, Marti Olsen. *The Introvert Advantage: How to Thrive in an Extrovert World*. New York: Workman Publishing, 2002.

Leaf, Dr. Caroline. *Who Switched Off My Brain? Controlling Toxic Thoughts and Emotions*. Switch on Your Brain USA, 2007.

Lewis, C.S. *The Four Loves*. London: Fount Paperbacks, 1960.

Loehr, Jim and Tony Schwartz. *The Power of Full Engagement: Managing Energy, Not Time, Is the Key to High Performance and Personal Renewal*. New York: Free Press, 2003.

Malandro, Loretta. *Say It Right the First Time*. New York: McGraw-Hill, 2003.

Martin, Roger. *The Responsibility Virus: How Control Freaks, Shrinking Violets—and the Rest of Us—Can Harness the Power of True Partnership*. New York: Basic Books, 2002.

Maruska, Don. *How Great Decisions Get Made: 10 Easy Steps for Reaching Agreement on Even the Toughest Issues*. New York: Amacom, 2004.

Moltmann, Jurgen. *Theology of Hope: A Contemporary Christian Eschatology*. Toronto: HarperCollins Canada, 1991.

Muller, Wayne. *Sabbath: Finding Rest, Renewal, and Delight in Our Busy Lives*. New York: Bantam Books, 1999.

Niebuhr, Reinhold. *Love and Justice: Selections from the Shorter Writings of Reinhold Niebuhr*. Louisville: Westminster John Knox Press, 1957.

Noddings, Nel. *The Challenge to Care in Schools: An Alternative Approach to Education*. New York: Teachers College Press, 2005.

Peck, M. Scott. *The Road Less Traveled: A New Psychology of Love, Traditional Values and Spiritual Growth* New York: Simon & Schuster, 1978.

Pink, Daniel H. *Drive: The Surprising Truth About What Motivates Us*. New York: Riverhead Books, 2009.

Quinn, Robert E. *Deep Change: Discovering the Leader Within*. San Francisco: Jossey-Bass, 1996.

Rath, Tom and Donald O. Clifton. *How Full Is Your Bucket?* New York: Gallup Press, 2004.

Rock, David. *Quiet Leadership: Six Steps to Transforming Performance at Work*. New York: HarperCollins, 2006.

Seligman, Martin E. P. *Authentic Happiness: Using the New Positive Psychology to Realize Your Potential for Lasting Fulfillment*. New York: Free Press, 2002.

Senge, Peter M. *The Fifth Discipline: The Art and Practice of the Learning Organization*. New York: Doubleday, 1990.

Senge, Peter M., Art Kleiner (ed.), Charlotte Roberts, Richard Ross, George Roth, and Bryan Smith. *The Dance of Change: The Challenges to Sustaining Momentum in Learning Organizations*. New York: Doubleday, 1999.

Senge, Peter M., Art Kleiner, Charlotte Roberts, Richard Ross, and Bryan Smith. *The Fifth Discipline Fieldbook: Strategies and Tools for Building a Learning Organization*. New York: Doubleday, 1994.

Senge, Peter M., C. Otto Scharmer, Joseph Jaworski, Betty Sue Flowers. *Presence: An Exploration of Profound Change in People, Organizations, and Society*. New York: Doubleday, 2004.

Shaw, Edward. *The Six Pillars of Reality-Based Training*. Minneapolis: Lakewood Publications, 1997.

Smalley, Gary and John Trent. *The Language of Love: How to Quickly Communicate Your Feelings and Needs*. Pomona, CA: Focus on the Family Publishing, 1988.

Stone, Douglas, Bruce Patton, Sheila Heen, and Roger Fisher. *Difficult Conversations: How to Discuss What Matters Most*. New York: Viking, 1999.

Tournier, Paul. *To Understand Each Other*. Louisville: Westminster John Knox Press, 2000.

Twenge, Jean M. and W. Keith Campbell. *The Narcissism Epidemic: Living in the Age of Entitlement*. New York: Free Press, 2010.

Ueland, Brenda. *Strength to Your Sword Arm: Selected Writings*. Duluth: Holy Cow! Press, 1993.

Vella, Jane. *Learning to Listen, Learning to Teach: The Power of Dialogue in Educating Adults*. San Francisco: Jossey-Bass, 1994.

Wheatley, Margaret J. *Leadership and the New Science: Learning About Organization from an Orderly Universe*. San Francisco: Berrett-Koehler, 1999.

Wheatley, Margaret J. *Turning to One Another: Simple Conversations to Restore Hope to the Future*. San Francisco: Berrett-Koehler, 2002.

Zimbardo, Philip and John Boyd. *The Time Paradox: The New Psychology of Time That Will Change Your Life*. New York: Free Press, 2008.

ARTICLES AND REPORTS

Aldag, Ray and Wayne Reschke. "Employee Value Added: Measuring Discretionary Effort and Its Value to the Organization." Center for Organization Effectiveness, 1997.

BlessingWhite. Employee Engagement Report 2005.

Boulay, Art. "Malden Mills: A Study in Leadership." *Quality Monitor Newsletter*, October 1996.

Conger, Jay A. "The Necessary Art of Persuasion." *Harvard Business Review*, May 1998.

Cooperrider, David L. "Positive Image, Positive Action: The Affirmative Basis of Organizing." Srivasta, Suresh (ed.) and David L. Cooperrider. *Appreciative Management and Leadership: The Power of Positive Thought and Action in Organizations* (rev. ed.) San Francisco: Jossey-Bass, 1990.

Corporate Leadership Council. Driving Performance and Retention Through Employee Engagement. Washington: Corporate Executive Board, 2004.

Corporate Leadership Council. 2002 Performance Management Survey. Washington: Corporate Executive Board, 2002.

Bibliography

Davey, Liane, Nancy Gore, and Owen Parker. "Reaching Productive Engagement: The Four Pillar Approach to Managing Investment in Human Capital." *Ivey Business Journal*, July–August 2003.

Goodridge, Elisabeth. "Six-hour Shifts Satisfied Kellogg's Appetite for Productivity." *Information Week*, April 8, 2002. http://www.informationweek.com/news/showArticle.jhtml ?articleID=6502155

Hallowell, Edward M. "The Human Moment at Work." *Harvard Business Review*, January 1, 1999.

Hodges, Michael. "Robert Thompson: He Goes to the Head of the Class for Dedication to Help Educate Detroit Children." *The Detroit News*, http://detnews.com/article/20090328/ SPECIAL02/903280338/Robert-Thompson--He-goes-to-the-head-of-the-class-for-dedication-to-help-educate-Detroit-children.

Hoover, Gretchen. "Maintaining Employee Engagement When Communicating Difficult Issues." *Communication World*, November–December 2005.

Jobs, Steve. "You've Got to Find What You Love." *Stanford Report*, June 14, 2005. http:/news.stanford.edu/news/2005/june15/ jobs.061505.html.

Kandath, Krishna, John Oetzel, Everett Rogers, and Ann Mayer-Guell. "Conflict in Virtual Communication." San Francisco: International Association of Business Communicators, 2005.

Kegan, Robert and Lisa Laskow Lahey. "The Real Reason People Won't Change." *Harvard Business Review*, November 2001.

Kinni, Theodore. "Is One-Dimensional Communication Limiting Your Leadership?" *Harvard Business Review*, May 2003.

Kofman, Fred and Peter M. Senge. "Communities of Commitment: The Heart of Learning Organizations." Chawla, Sarita and John Renesch (eds.). *Learning Organizations: Developing Cultures for Tomorrow's Workplace*. Portland: Productivity Press, 1995.

Lagace, Martha, "High Commitment, High Performance Management." *Harvard Business School Working Knowledge*, August 10, 2009.

Bibliography

Melcrum. Employee Engagement: How to Build a High-Performance Workforce. Melcrum Publishing, 2005.

Rogen International. "Balancing E-mail and Face to Face in Workplace Communication." March–April 2001.

Rogers, Carl R. "A Theory of Therapy, Personality, and Interpersonal Relationships, as Developed in the Client-Centered Framework." In S. Koch (ed.). *Psychology: A Study of a Science* (vol. 3). New York: McGraw-Hill, 1959.

Shaw, Kieron. "An Engagement Strategy Process for Communicators." *Strategic Communication Management*, April–May 2005.

Towers Perrin. Reconnecting with Employees: Quantifying the Value of Engaging Your Workforce. 2005.

Towers Perrin. Ten Steps to Creating an Engaged Workforce: Key European Findings. Towers Perrin Global Workforce Study, 2005.

Towers Perrin. Working Today: Exploring Employees' Emotional Connections to Their Jobs. Towers Perrin/Gang & Gang, 2003.

Towers Perrin. Working Today: Understanding What Drives Employee Engagement. Towers Perrin/Gang & Gang, 2003.

Tucker, Elissa, Tina Kao, and Nidhi Verma. Next-Generation Talent Management: Insights on How Workforce Trends Are Changing the Face of Talent Management. Hewitt Associates, 2005.

Watson Wyatt Worldwide. Canadian Organizations Must Work Harder to Productively Engage Employees. Watson Wyatt's WorkCanada 2004–2005 Survey.

Withers, Pam. Retention Strategies That Respond to Worker Values. Workforce Management, July 2001.

Woodall, Katherine and Charlie Watts. "What 25,000 Employees Globally Say About Communication Effectiveness." Towers Perrin.

INDEX

ALSO BY BRADY G. WILSON

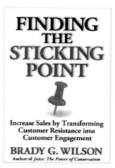

* Volume discounts available on all three of Brady's books. Contact us for more details.

* Engage in conversation with us to discover meaningful, proven strategies for your organization, by calling 1-888-822-5479.

* Visit the Juice Resource Centre at www.juiceinc.com for information about upcoming workshops and speaking engagements, articles, and excerpts, and additional Juice resources, including The Juice Check™ — a tool designed to help you measure how much intelligent energy is released in your work environment.

* Brady Wilson is a highly animated, intensely pragmatic presenter, trainer, and consultant. He is a gifted keynote presenter on the topics of Communication, Employee Engagement, and Emotional Intelligence at Work.

For more information about Brady Wilson or Juice Inc.:

phone: 1-888-822-5479 e-mail: info@juiceinc.com

www.juiceinc.com

LaVergne, TN USA
26 May 2010
183946LV00004B/5/P